Computation in Ancient India

Also by SUBHASH KAK

The Architecture of Knowledge
The Astronomical Code of the Ṛgveda
The Gods Within
Mind and Self
The Nature of Physical Reality
The Prajñā Sūtra: Aphorisms of Intuition
The Wishing Tree
In Search of the Cradle of Civilization
The Aśvamedha
Matter and Mind

Computation in Ancient India

Edited by

T.R.N. Rao

Subhash Kak

Mount Meru Publishing

Library and Archives Canada Cataloguing in Publication
Computing science in ancient India
Computation in ancient India / [edited by] T.R.N. Rao, Subhash Kak.

Originally published under title: Computing science in ancient India.
Based on papers presented at the Louisiana Symposium on Ancient Indian Sciences, held on October 25, 1997, at Lafayette, Louisiana.
Includes bibliographical references and index.
Issued in print and electronic formats.
ISBN 978-1-988207-12-4 (paperback).--ISBN 978-1-988207-11-7 (HTML)

1. Hindu mathematics. 2. Mathematics, Ancient--India. 3. Computer science--India--Mathematics. I. Kak, Subhash, 1947-, editor II. Rao, T. R. N. Thammavarapu R. N.), 1933-, editor III. Louisiana Symposium on Ancient Indian Sciences (1997: Lafayette, La.) IV. Title.

QA27.I4C65 2016 510'.934 C2016-904264-2
C2016-904265-0

Published in 2016 by:
Mount Meru publishing
P.O. Box 30026
Cityside Postal Outlet PO
Mississauga, Ontario
Canada L4Z 0B6
Email: mountmerupublishing@gmail.com

ISBN 978-1-988207-12-4
Front cover and Back cover images: Courtesy DARPA (Defense Advanced Research Projects Agency)

Contents

Preface

Our understanding of how ideas of computing and mathematics first arose has changed a great deal in the past few years. But this understanding has not filtered down to the computer scientist, let alone popular consciousness. It is to address this need that this sourcebook has been put together.

The material in the book must be taken as an introduction to the Indian contributions to the science of computing. We have taken contributions from different time periods, ranging from the Vedic to the medieval. Apart from chapters that deal with computing techniques, we also include material on astronomy, cosmology, and cognitive science that tell us something about the problem areas where the computing science notions were applied. It is hoped that these chapters will provide a flavor of Indian science so that the interested reader can learn about other topics by examining papers that are referenced at the end of the chapters.

The book starts with an overview of Indian science (Kak). The next three chapters deal with the description of binary numbers (van Nooten), the *Kaṭapayādi* notation and its equivalence to hashing that is used in computer systems (Raman), and the Pāṇini-Backus form to describe a high-level computer language based on the ideas of the great grammarian Pāṇini (Rao).

The next two chapters (Staal) describe some technical aspects of Pāṇini's grammar and Indian logic. Note that the Pāṇinian structure (5th century BCE) has been shown to be equivalent to the Turing machine and the rise of mathematical logic in India took place centuries before its rediscovery in Europe!

The next chapter (Frawley) shows how one needs ingenuity in decoding Indian texts. It is shown that Indian myths represent information regarding the motions of the planets. The last two chapters (Kak) deal with cosmology and cognitive science.

The immediate inspiration for this book came from the Louisiana Symposium on Ancient Indian Sciences that was held in Lafayette, Louisiana on October 25, 1997. The symposium was sponsored jointly by the University of Southwestern Louisiana (USL), Acadian Indian Association (AIA), and the World Association of Vedic Sciences (WAVES). Participants from the U.S., Britain, and India took part in the symposium and it was decided that a sourcebook of early Indian contributions to computing science be put together.

Many individuals have contributed through financial and organizational support in arranging the Louisiana Symposium on Ancient Indian Sciences and in publication of this book and we acknowledge their support. We also acknowledge the patient work of Roxie Guidry in putting these chapters together and obtaining the necessary copyright permissions from the authors and journals.

The original edition was published with the title *Computing Science in Ancient India* by Munshiram Manoharlal in New Delhi in 2000 but it has been out of print for several years. The book is still in demand hence this new edition. We have modified the title somewhat by replacing “computing science” by “computation”, since the latter term is more inclusive and can be taken to imply a computational approach to not only numerical computation but also to problems of logic and cognitive science.

As in the previous edition, we have decided to let the articles retain different schemes to represent Sanskrit words.

T.R.N. Rao and Subhash Kak

Introduction

Subhash Kak

Computer science is entering a new threshold where insights from biology, psychology, and physics are being harnessed to understand how nature performs some computations better than any machine. As we prepare for the future, it is also meaningful to look back into the beginnings of this science. This is what takes us to India.

Historical research of the past two or three decades has shown that the key ideas of computer science arose in India. Everyone knows that the sign for zero was invented in India about two thousand years ago (e.g. Ifrah 1985). It is much less known that important concepts like that of recursion, algebraic transformation, mathematical logic, abstract language description, binary numbers, combinatorics also arose in India several centuries before their rediscovery in the West.

The Indian culture area provides us extensive material, across a very broad time-span, to help us understand the earliest history of ideas. The ancient Indian texts are layered in such a fashion that we can see the gradual development of mathematical, physical, linguistic, and psychological ideas (e.g. Feuerstein et al 1995: Seidenberg 1978: Staal 1988). We find that the ancient Indians were greatly interested in computing methods in geometry, astronomy, grammar, music and other fields. They were also interested in cognitive science where they were so advanced that their insights may yet be useful to modern science.

The understanding of the chronological framework of the Indian civilization has changed greatly in the last few years due to revolutionary discoveries in art and archaeology.

Art

The earliest Indic art (Figure 1) is preserved on rocks in the paleolithic, mesolithic and neolithic stages (40,000 BCE onwards) and the seals and the sculpture of the Indus-Sarasvati phase which lasted from about 8000 BCE to 1900 BCE According to Wakankar, the beginnings of the rock art have been traced to 40,000 years BP (before present) in the decorated ostrich eggshells from Rajasthan, dated using radiocarbon techniques.

Subsequent phases have been determined using evolution of style and other radiocarbon dates. The mesolithic period has been dated as 12.000 to 6000 BP. A distribution of the sites of the rock art is given in Figure 2.

The earliest drawings of Figure 1 are characterized by dynamic action, vitality in form, and an acute insight into abstraction and visual perception.

It has been found that there is significant continuity of motif in the rock art and the later Indus-Sarasvati civilization indicating an unbroken link with the paleolithic and the mesolithic cultures of India.

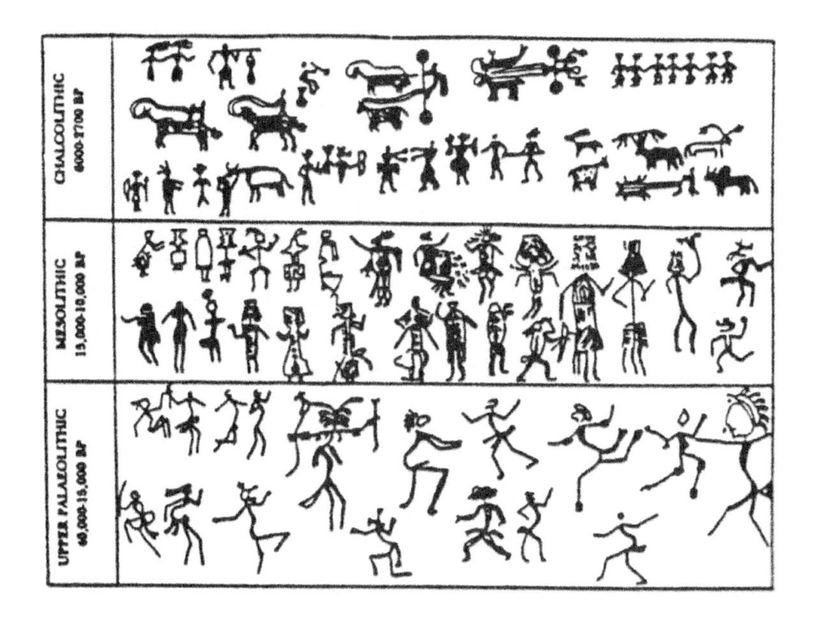

Figure 1. Evolution of Indian rock art according to Wakankar (1992)

Figure 3 shows tessellations from the ancient rock art of India. G.S. Tyagi (1992) has argued that these designs occur at the lowest stratum of the rock paintings and if that is accepted they belong to the upper paleolithic period. These designs are unique to India in the ancient world. Tyagi has suggested that they may represent a "trance experience."

The basic feature of these tessellations is infinite repetition. This repetition may occur for a basic pattern or, more abstractly, the lines extend spatially in a manner so that a basic pattern is repeated in two directions.

Figure 2. Rock art sites in india

An understanding of this abstract concept must have been a part of the thought system of the artists. This is another continuity with the central place of the notion of infinite in later Indian thought.

The abstract and the iconic elements in Indian rock art are different from the more naturalistic ancient European cave paintings. There is also difference in the nature of the community and the state in the Western and the Indian civilizations in the earliest urban phase. The West has monumental temples, tombs, palaces whereas the society in India appears to have been governed by a sacred order.

Figure 3. Tessellations in ancient Indian rock art

Literature

One aspect of the Indian literary tradition, which is at least four thousand years old, is its imagination. The epic *Mahābhārata* mentions embryo transplantation, multiple births from the same fetus, battle with extra-terrestrials who are wearing air-tight suits, and weapons of mass-destruction. The *Rāmāyaṇa* mentions air travel. The *Bhāgavata Purāṇa,* a medieval encyclopaedic text, has episodes related to different passage of time for different observers, which is very similar to what happens in the theory of relativity.

The notion of self in the *Upaniṣads* embodies a very subtle understanding of observers and of reality. The *Yoga Vāsiṣṭha* and the *Tripurārahasya* present a deep discussion of the nature of consciousness.

Puranic cosmology gives an age of the universe that is in close agreement with the modern value. We find examples of accurate astronomical numbers in the early texts. Perhaps, this accuracy was due to the knowledge of biological cycles that reflect astronomical processes, such as menses according to the period of the moon. The understanding of the outer was helped along by an understanding of the inner.

Are these examples similar to the science fiction imagination of our own times? There is no evidence of a material science that could have spawned such imagination. The Indian texts are either full of the most astonishingly lucky guesses or we have not yet understood their knowledge framework.

Science

Our understanding of Indian science has improved greatly in the last twenty years. In the Vedic times itself the notions of rule and metarule emerged. Subsequently, not only the sign for zero, but also the binary number system, algebraic transformation, recursion, hashing, mathematical logic, formal grammars and high level language description arose first in India. These ideas helped foster a keen study of astronomy, medicine, physics, psychology, linguistics, and the nature of mind.

The two greatest names in the earliest phase of Indian computing and mathematical sciences are Pāṇini and Piṅgala. Pāṇini created an abstract grammar for Sanskrit which in its computing power is as powerful as any computing machine, whereas Piṅgala described the binary number system in his text on meters. There is an old Indian tradition that describes Pāṇini and Piṅgala as brothers (Shrava, 1977) and there is no reason for us to doubt it.

V.S. Agarwal in his majesterial *India as Known to Pāṇini* (1953) adequately reviewed the question of the chronology of Pāṇini. A variety of evidence indicates that he lived in the 5th Century BCE. Indian computation science had already reached a high degree of maturity 2,500 years ago!

References

Agarwala, V.S. 1953. *India as Known to Pāṇini.* Lucknow.

Feuerstein, G., Kak, S., Frawley, D. 1995. *In Search of the Cradle of Civilization.* Wheaton.

Ifrah, G. 1985. *From One to Zero.* New York.

Seidenberg, A. 1978. The origin of mathematics. *Archive for History of Exact Sciences.* 18, 301-342.

Shrava, Satya. 1977. *A Comprehensive History of Vedic Literature: Brahmana and Aranyaka Works.* Delhi.

Staal, F. 1988. *Universals.* Chicago.

Tyagi, G.S. 1992. "Decorative intricate patterns in Indian rock art." in *Rock Art in the Old World.* ed. M. Lorblanchet, 303-317. New Delhi.

Wakankar, V.S. 1992. "Rock painting in India." in *Rock Art in the Old World*, ed. M. Lorblanchet. 319-336. New Delhi.

An Overview of Ancient Indian Science

Subhash Kak

The Indian tradition looks at its own heritage as the "way of science." The earliest part of its remembrance is lauded as the *"Veda,"* a word which means knowledge. Some scholars have looked at this claim with suspicion, suggesting that this knowledge amounted to no more than metaphysical speculations. But new findings in archaeology, astronomy, history of science and Vedic scholarship have shown that the traditional view is substantially correct. We now know that Vedic knowledge embraced physics, mathematics, astronomy, logic, cognition and other disciplines. We find that Vedic science is the earliest science that has come down to mankind. This has significant implications in our understanding of the history of ideas and the evolution of early civilizations.

The reconstructions of our earliest science are based not only on the *Vedas* but also on their appendices called the *Vedāṅgas.* The six *Vedāṅgas* deal with *kalpa,* performance of ritual with its basis of geometry, mathematics and calendrics; *śikṣā,* phonetics; *chandas,* metrical structures; *nirukta,* etymology; *vyākaraṇa,* grammar; and *jyotiṣa,* astronomy and other cyclical phenomena. Then there are naturalistic descriptions in the various Vedic books that tell us a lot about scientific ideas of those times.

Briefly, the Vedic texts present a tripartite and recursive world view. The universe is viewed as three regions of earth, space, and sky with the corresponding entities of Agni, Indra, and Viśve Devāḥ (all gods). Counting separately the joining regions leads to a total of five categories where, as we see in Figure 1, water separates earth and fire, and air separates fire and ether.

In Vedic ritual the three regions are assigned different fire altars. Furthermore, the five categories are represented in terms of altars of five layers. The great altars were built of a thousand bricks to a variety of dimensions which coded astronomical knowledge (Kak 1994a; 1995a,b).

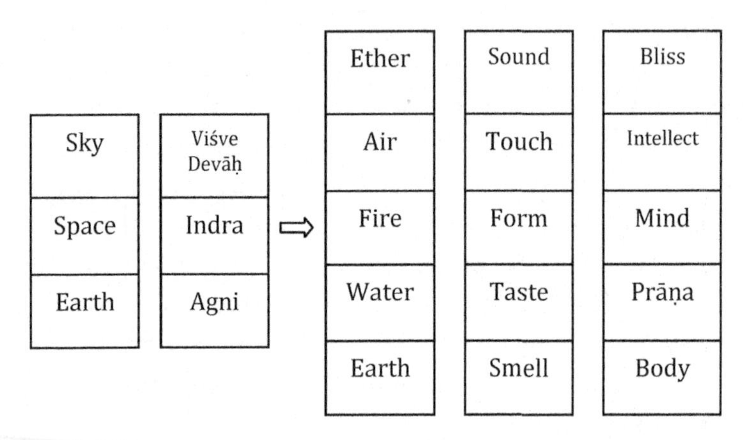

Figure 1. From the tripartite model to five categories of analysis.

In the Vedic world view, the processes in the sky, on earth, and within the mind are taken to be connected. The Vedic rishis were aware that all descriptions of the universe lead to logical paradox. The one category transcending all oppositions was termed *brahman*. Understanding the nature of consciousness was of paramount importance in this view but this did not mean that other sciences were ignored. Vedic ritual was a symbolic retelling of this world view.

Chronology

To place Vedic science in context it is necessary to have a proper understanding of the chronology of the Vedic literature. There are astronomical references in the *Vedas* which recall events in the third or the fourth millennium BCE and earlier. The recent discovery (e.g. Feuerstein 1995) that Sarasvati, the preeminent river of the Rigvedic times, went dry around 1900 BCE due to tectonic upheavals implies that the *Rigveda* is to be dated prior to this epoch, perhaps prior to 2000 BCE, since the literature that immediately followed the *Rigveda* does not speak of any geological catastrophe. But we cannot be very precise about our estimates. There exist traditional accounts in the *Purāṇas* that assign greater antiquity to the *Rigveda:* for example, the Kaliyuga tradition speaks of 3100 BCE and the Varahamihira tradition mentions 2400 BCE. According to Henri-Paul Francfort (1992) of the Indo-French team that surveyed this area, the Sarasvati river had ceased to be a perennial river by the third millennium BCE; this supports those who argue for the older dates. But in the absence of conclusive evidence, it is prudent to take the most conservative of these dates, namely 2000 BCE as the latest period to be associated with the *Rigveda.*

The textbook accounts of the past century or so were based on the now disproven supposition that the *Rigveda* is to be dated to about 1500-1000 BCE and, therefore, the question of the dates assigned to the *Brāhmaṇas, Sūtras* and other literature remains open. The detailed chronology of the literature that followed *Rigveda* has not yet been worked out. A chronology of this literature was attempted based solely on the internal astronomical evidence in the important book *Ancient Indian Chronology* by the historian of science P.C.

Sengupta in 1947. Although Sengupta's dates have the virtue of inner consistency, they have neither been examined carefully by other scholars nor checked against archaeological evidence.

This means that we can only speak in the most generalities regarding the chronology of the texts: assign *Rigveda* to the third millennium BCE and earlier and the *Brāhmaṇas* to the second millennium. This also implies that the archaeological finds of the Indus-Sarasvati period, which are coeval with *Rigveda* literature, can be used to cross-check textual evidence.

Note also that archaeological discoveries have established that the Indian tradition can be traced back to at least 8000 BCE. The much old rock art tradition goes back to 40,000 BCE. Furthermore, there is no evidence of any break in the skeletal record during the period 4500-800 BCE or any eastward invasions of people before 1900 BCE. According to Kennedy (1995), "There is no evidence of demographic disruptions in the north-western sector of the subcontinent during and immediately after the decline of the Harappan culture." Shaffer and Lichtenstein (1995), speaking of the migrations caused by the drying up of the Sarasvati river, say, "This shift by Harappan and, perhaps, other Indus Valley cultural mosaic groups, is the only archaeologically documented west-to- east movement of human populations in South Asia before the first half of the first millennium B.C." This, together with a host of other evidence, compels the view that the archaeological record and the Vedic literary texts refer to the same reality. Figure 2, adapted from Lal (1997), shows the picture in India during the fourth and the third millennia BCE.

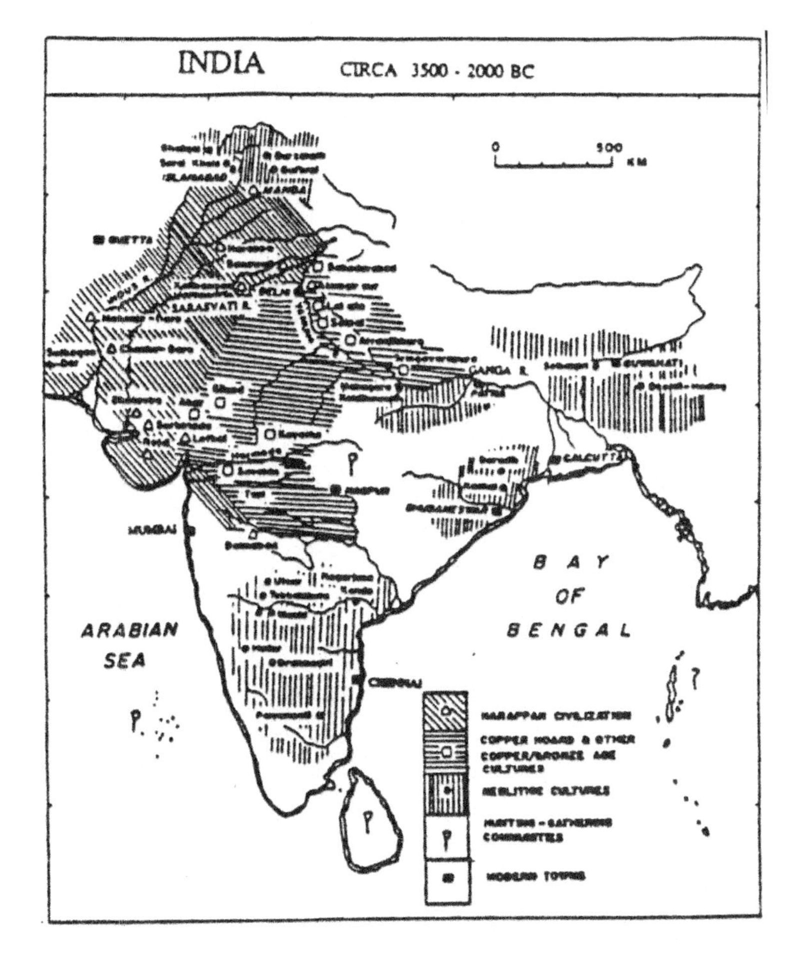

Figure 2

No comprehensive studies of ancient Indian science exist. The textbook accounts like the one to be found in Basham's *The Wonder that was India* are hopelessly out of date. But there are some excellent surveys of selected material. The task of putting it all together into a comprehensive whole will be a major task for historians of science.

This essay presents an assortment of topics from Indian science. We review mathematics, astronomy, grammar, logic and medicine.

Vedic Cognitive Science

The *Rigveda* speaks of cosmic order. It is assumed that there exist equivalencies of various kinds between the outer and the inner worlds. It is these connections that make it possible for our minds to comprehend the universe. It is noteworthy that the analytical methods are used both in the examination of the outer world as well as the inner world. This allowed the Vedic rishis to place in sharp focus paradoxical aspects of analytical knowledge. Such paradoxes have become only too familiar to the contemporary scientist in all branches of inquiry.

In the Vedic view, the complementary nature of the mind and the outer world, is of fundamental significance. Knowledge is classified in two ways: the lower or dual: and the higher or unified. What this means is that knowledge is superficially dual and paradoxical but at a deeper level it has a unity. The Vedic view claims that the material and the conscious are aspects of the same transcendental reality.

The idea of complementarity was at the basis of the systematization of Indian philosophic traditions as well, so that complementary approaches were paired together. We have the groups of: logic (*nyāya*) and physics (*vaiśeṣika*), cosmology (*sāṅkhya*) and psychology (*yoga*), and language (*mīmāṃsā*) and reality (*vedānta*). Although these philosophical schools were formalized in the post-Vedic age, we find an echo of these ideas in the Vedic texts.

In the Rigveda there is reference to the yoking of the horses to the chariot of Indra, Ashvins, or Agni; and we are told elsewhere that these gods represent the essential mind. The same metaphor of the chariot for a person is encountered in Kaṭha Upaniṣad and the Bhagavad Gītā; this chariot is pulled in different directions by the horses, representing senses, which are yoked to it. The mind is the driver who holds the reins to these horses; but next to the mind sits the true observer, the self, who represents a universal unity. Without this self no coherent behaviour is possible. In the *Taittirīya Upaniṣad,* the individual is represented in terms of five different sheaths or levels that enclose the individual's self.

The *sāṅkhya* and the *yoga* systems take the mind as consisting of five components: *manas, ahaṅkāra, citta, buddhi,* and *ātman. Manas* is the lower mind which collects sense impressions. Its perceptions shift from moment to moment. This sensory-motor mind obtains its inputs from the senses of hearing, touch, sight, taste, and smell. Each of these senses may be taken to be governed by a separate agent. *Ahaṅkāra* is the sense of I-ness that associates some perceptions to a subjective and personal experience. Once sensory impressions have been related to I-ness by *ahankara,* their evaluation and resulting decisions are arrived at by *buddhi,* the intellect. *Manas, ahankara,* and *buddhi* are collectively called the internal instruments of the mind.

Citta is the memory bank of the mind. These memories constitute the foundation on which the rest of the mind operates. But *citta* is not merely a passive instrument. The organization of the new impressions throws up instinctual or primitive urges which creates different emotional states.

This mental complex surrounds the innermost aspect of consciousness which is called *ātman*, the self, *brahman*, or jīva. *Ātman* is considered to be beyond a finite enumeration of categories.

Mathematical and Physical Sciences

Geometry and Mathematics

Seidenberg, by examining the evidence in the *Śatapatha Brāhmaṇa*, showed that Indian geometry predates Greek geometry by centuries. Seidenberg (1962) argues that the birth of geometry and mathematics had a ritual origin. For example, the earth was represented by a circular altar and the heavens were represented by a square altar and the ritual consisted of converting the circle into a square of an identical area. There we see the beginnings of geometry!

Seidenberg considered two aspects of the "Pythagoras" theorem in the Vedic literature. One aspect is purely algebraic that presents numbers a, b, c for which $a^2 + b^2 = c^2$. The second is the geometric, according to which the sum of the areas of two square areas of different size is equal to another square. Seidenberg argued that the Babylonians knew the algebraic aspect of this theorem as early as 1700 BCE, but they did not seem to know the geometric aspect. The *Śatapatha Brāhmaṇa*, which precedes the age of Pythagoras, knows both aspects. Therefore, the Indians could not have learnt it from the Old-Babylonians or the Greeks, who claim to have rediscovered the result only with Pythagoras.

In his paper on the origin of mathematics, Seidenberg (1978) concluded: "Old-Babylonia [1700 BC] got the theorem of Pythagoras from India or that both Old-Babylonia and India got it from a third source. Now the Sanskrit scholars do not give me a date so far back as 1700 B.C. Therefore I postulate a pre-Old-Babylonian (i.e., pre-1700 B.C.) source of the kind of geometric rituals we see preserved in the *Sulvasutras*, or at least for the mathematics involved in these rituals." That was before archaeological finds disproved the earlier assumption of a break in Indian civilization in the second millennium BCE; it was this assumption of the Sanskritists that led Seidenberg to postulate a third earlier source. Now with our new knowledge, Seidenberg's conclusion of India being the source of the geometric and mathematical knowledge of the ancient world fits in with the new chronology of the texts.

Astronomy

Using hitherto neglected texts related to ritual and the Vedic indices, an astronomy of the third millennium BCE has been discovered (Kak 1994a, 1995a,b). Here the altars symbolized different parts of the year. In one ritual, pebbles were placed around the altars for the earth, the atmosphere, and the sky. The number of these pebbles were 21, 78, and 261, respectively. These numbers add up to the 360 days of the year. There were other features related to the design of the altars which suggested that the ritualists were aware that the length of the year was between 365 and 366 days.

The organization of the Vedic books was also according to an astronomical code. To give just one simple example, the total number of verses in all the *Vedas* is 20,358 which equals 261 × 78, a product of the sky and atmosphere numbers! The Vedic ritual followed the seasons hence the importance of astronomy.

The second millennium text *Vedāṅga Jyotiṣa* went beyond the earlier calendrical astronomy to develop a theory for the mean motions of the sun and the moon. This marked the beginnings of the application of mathematics to the motions of the heavenly bodies.

The sun was taken to be midway in the skies. A considerable amount of Vedic mythology regarding the struggle between the demons and the gods is a metaphorical retelling of the motions of Venus and Mars (Frawley 1994).

The famous myth of Vishnu's three strides measuring the universe becomes intelligible when we note that early texts equate Vishnu and Mercury. The myth appears to celebrate the first measurement of the period of Mercury (Kak 1996a) since three periods equals the number assigned in altar ritual to the heavens. Other arguments suggest that the Vedic people knew the periods of the five classical planets.

Yājñavalkya (1800 BCE ?) knew of a 95-year cycle to harmonize the motions of the sun and the moon and he also knew that the sun's circuit was asymmetric (Kak 1997c).

Writing

Cryptological analysis has revealed that the Brahmi script of the Mauryan times evolved out of the third millennium Sarasvati (Indus) script. The Sarasvati script was perhaps the first true alphabetic script although it used a large number of logographic symbols as well. The worship of Sarasvati as the goddess of learning remembers the development of writing on the banks of the Sarasvati river. It also appears that the symbol for zero was derived from the fish sign that stood for "ten" in Brahmi and this occurred around 50 BCE- 50 CE (Kak 1994b).

Binary Numbers

Barend van Nooten (1993) has shown that binary numbers were known at the time of Piṅgala's *Chandaḥśāstra*. Piṅgala, who lived around the early first century BCE used binary numbers to classify Vedic meters. The knowledge of binary numbers indicates a deep understanding of arithmetic. A binary representation requires the use of only two symbols, rather than the ten required in the usual decimal representation, and it has now become the basis of information storage in terms of sequences of 0s and 1s in modern-day computers.

Music

Ernest McClain (1978) has described the tonal basis of early myth. McClain argues that the connections between music and myth are even deeper than astronomy and myth. The invariances at the basis of tones could very well have served as the ideal for the development of the earliest astronomy. The tonal invariances of music may have suggested the search of similar invariances in the heavenly phenomena.

The *Sāmaveda*, where the hymns were supposed to be sung, was compared to the sky. Apparently, this comparison was to emphasize the musical basis of astronomy. The Vedic hymns are according to a variety of meters; but what purpose, if any, lay behind a specific choice is unknown.

Grammar

Pāṇini's grammar (5th century BCE or earlier) provides 4,000 rules that describe the Sanskrit of his day completely. This grammar is acknowledged to be one of the greatest intellectual achievements of all time. The great variety of language mirrors, in many ways, the complexity of nature. It is remarkable that Pāṇini set out to describe the entire grammar in terms of a finite number of rules. Frits Staal (1988) has shown that the grammar of Pāṇini represents a universal grammatical and computing system. From this perspective it anticipates the logical framework of modern computers (Kak 1987). One may speak of a Pāṇini machine as a model for the most powerful computing system.

Medicine

Indian medicine builds upon the tripartite Vedic approach to the world. It is noteworthy that there is a close parallel between Indian and Greek medicine. For example, the idea of breath (*prāṇa* in Sanskrit, and *pneuma* in Greek) is central to both. Jean Filliozat (1970) has argued that the idea of the correct association between the three elements of the wind, the gall, and the phlegm, which was described first by Plato in Greek medicine, appears to be derived from the earlier *tridosha* theory of Ayurveda. Filliozat suggests that the transmission occurred via the Persian empire.

Rhythms of Life

The moon is called the "lord of speech" in the *Rigveda*. Other many references suggest that in the Rigvedic times the moon was taken to be connected with the mind. This is stated most directly in the famous Puruśasūkta, the Cosmic Man hymn, of the *Rigveda* where it is stated that the mind is born of the moon. It appears that the relationships between the astronomical and the terrestrial were also taken in terms of periodicities and so there was knowledge of biological cycles (Kak 1996b, 1997).

What are the seats of these cycles? According to *tantra*, the *cakras* of the body are the centers of the different elements as well as cognitive capacities and rhythms related to "internal planets." The knowledge of these rhythms appears to have led to astrology.

Cosmology

We have seen how the logical apparatus that was brought to bear on the outer world was applied to the analysis of the mind. But the question remains: How does inanimate matter come to have awareness? This metaphysical question was answered by postulating entities for smell, taste, form, touch, and sound as in Figure 1. In the Sāṅkhya system, a total of twenty-four such categories are assumed. These categories are supposed to emerge at the end of a long chain of evolution and they may be considered to be material. The breath of life into the instruments of sight, touch, hearing, and so on is provided by the twenty-fifth category, which is *puruṣa*, the soul. The *tanmātra* of Sāṅkhya is the potentiality that leads to matter or cognitive centers. In this conception it is somewhat like a quantum potential.

The recursive Vedic world-view requires that the universe itself go through cycles of creation and destruction. This view became a part of the astronomical framework and ultimately very long cycles of billions of years were assumed. The Sāṅkhya evolution takes the life forms to evolve into an increasingly complex system until the end of the cycle.

The categories of Sankhya operate at the level of the individual as well. Life mirrors the entire creation cycle and cognition mirrors a life-history. Surprisingly similar are the modern slogan: ontogeny is phylogeny, and microgeny (the cognitive process) is a speeded-up ontogeny (Brown 1994). The Vaiśeṣika system describes an atomic world.

Science after Āryabhaṭa

In the earliest period of Indian science, it is exceptional when we know the authorship of a text or an idea. For example, although Yājñavalkya and Lagadha describe considerable astronomy, we do not know if this was developed by them or they merely summarized what was then well known. Likewise we are not sure of the individual contributions in the Śulba Sūtras — of Baudhāyana, Āpastamba, and other authors — which describe geometry, or in Piṅgala's Chandaḥśāstra which shows how to count in a binary manner. The major exception to the anonymous nature of early Indian science is the grammatical tradition starting with Pāṇini. This tradition is an application of the scientific method where the infinite variety of linguistic data is generated by means of a limited number of rules.

With Āryabhaṭa, we enter a new phase in which it becomes easier to trace the authorship of specific ideas. But even here there remain other aspects which are not so well understood. For example, the evolution of Indian medicine is not as well documented as that of Indian mathematics. Neither do we understand well the manner in which the philosophical basis underlying Indian science evolved.

Thus many texts speak of the relativity of time and space—abstract concepts that developed in the scientific context just a hundred years ago. The Puranas speak of countless universes, time flowing at different rates for different observers and so on.

The Mahābhārata speaks of an embryo being divided into one hundred parts each becoming after maturation in a separate pot, a healthy baby; this is how the Kaurava brothers are born. There is also mention of an embryo. conceived in one womb, being transferred to the womb of another woman from where it is born: the transferred embryo is Balarāma and this is how he is a brother to Krishna although he was born to Rohiṇi and not to Devaki. There is an ancient mention of space travelers wearing airtight suits in the epic Mahābhārata which may be classified as an early form of science fiction.

Universes defined recursively are described in the famous episode of Indra and the ants in *Brahmavaivarta Purāṇa*. Here Viṣṇu in the guise of a boy, explains to Indra that the ants he sees walking on the ground have all been Indras in their own solar systems in different times! These flights of imagination are to be traced to more than a straightforward generalization of the motions of the planets into a cyclic universe. They must be viewed in the background of an amazingly sophisticated tradition of cognitive and analytical thought (see e.g. Staal 1998).

The context of modern science fiction books is clear: it is the liberation of the earlier modes of thought by the revolutionary developments of the 20th century science and technology. But how was science fiction integrated into the mainstream of Indian literary tradition two thousand years ago? What was the intellectual ferment in which such sophisticated ideas arose?

Of the eighteen early siddhantas the summaries of only five are available now. In addition to these siddhantas, practical manuals, astronomical tables, description of instruments, and other miscellaneous writings have also come down to us (Sarma 1985). The Puranas also have some material on astronomy. Here we just list some of the main names in astronomy after 450 CE. For background on astronomy, see Billard (1971) and Selenius (1978); for a review of the contributions to mathematical logic, see Matilal (1968) and Staal (1988).

Āryabhaṭa (born 476) is the author of the first of the later siddhantas called *Āryabhaṭīyam* which sketches his mathematical, planetary, and cosmic theories. This book is divided into four chapters:

i. the astronomical constants and the sine table
ii. mathematics required for computations
iii. division of time and rules for computing the longitudes of planets using eccentrics and epicycles
iv. the armillary sphere, rules relating to problems of trigonometry and the computation of eclipses.

The parameters of Āryabhaṭīyam have, as their origin, the commencement of Kaliyuga on Friday, 18th February, 3102 BCE. He wrote another book where the epoch is a bit different.

Āryabhaṭa took the earth to spin on its axis; this idea appears to have been his innovation. He also considered the heavenly motions to go through a cycle of 4.32 billion years; here he went with an older tradition, but he introduced a new scheme of subdivisions within this great cycle.

That Āryabhaṭa was aware of the relativity of motion is clear from this passage in his book, "Just as a man in a boat sees the trees on the bank move in the opposite direction, so an observer on the equator sees the stationary stars as moving precisely toward the west."

Varāhamihira

Varāhamihira (died 587) lived in Ujjain and he wrote three important books: *Pancasiddhāntika*, *Bṛhat Saṃhitā*, and *Bṛhat Jātaka*. The first is a summary of five early astronomical systems including the *Sūrya Siddhānta*. (Incidently, the modern *Sūrya Siddhānta* is different in many details from this ancient one.) Another system described by him, the *Paitāmaha Siddhānta*, appears to have many similarities with the ancient *Vedāṅga Jyotiṣa* of Lagadha.

Brihat Samhita is a compilation of an assortment of topics that provides interesting details of the beliefs of those times. Brihat Jataka is a book on astrology which appears to be considerably influenced by Greek astrology.

Brahmagupta

Brahmagupta of Bhilamala in Rajasthan, who was bom in 598, wrote his masterpiece, *Brahmasphuṭa Siddhānta* in 628. His school, which was a rival to that of Āryabhaṭa, has been very influential in western and northern India. Brahmagupta's work was translated into Arabic in 771 or 773 at Baghdad and it became famous in the Arabic world as Sindhind.

One of Brahmagupta's chief contributions is the solution of a certain second order indeterminate equation which is of great significance in number theory.

Another of his books, the *Khaṇḍakhādyaka*, remained a popular handbook for astronomical computations for centuries.

Bhāskara

Bhāskara (born 1114), who was from the Karnataka region, was an outstanding mathematician and astronomer. Amongst his mathematical contributions is the concept of differentials. He was the author of *Siddhānta Śiromaṇi*, a book in four parts:

i. Līlāvati on arithmetic
ii. Bījaganita on algebra
iii. Ganitādhyāya
iv. Golādhyāya on astronomy

His epicyclic-eccentric theories of planetary motions are more developed than in the earlier siddhantas.

Subsequent to Bhāskara we see a flourishing tradition of mathematics and astronomy in Kerala which saw itself as a successor to the school of Āryabhaṭa. We know of the contributions of very many scholars in this tradition, of whom we will speak only of two below.

Mādhava

Mādhava (c. 1340-1425) developed a procedure to determine the positions of the moon every 36 minutes. He also provided methods to estimate the motions of the planets. He gave power series expansions for trigonometric functions, and for pi correct to eleven decimal places.

Nīlakanṭha Somayāji

Nīlakanṭha (c. 1444-1545) was a very prolific scholar who wrote several works on astronomy. It appears that Nīlakanṭha found the correct formulation for the equation of the center of the planets and his model must be considered a true heliocentric model of the solar system. He also improved upon the power series techniques of Mādhava.

The methods developed by the Kerala mathematicians were far ahead of the European mathematics of the day.

Concluding Remarks

This brief overview is not systematic. Our objective was merely to highlight a few areas that show the need for a radical rewriting of the history of science in India. During the last couple of decades, overwhelming evidence has accumulated that shows mathematics and astronomy arose in India at least a thousand years sooner than had been earlier supposed. The cognitive tradition in India led to advanced theories of mind and the development of grammatical and computing systems. There are aspects of the Indian approach to consciousness which may yet be of value to contemporary science.

References

This list includes items not explicitly listed in the text where the brief notices in the paper are fully developed.

Billard, R. 1971. *L 'astronomie Indienne*. Paris.

Brown, J.W. 1994. Morphogenesis and mental process. *Development and Psychopathology*. vol. 6, 551-563.

Feuerstein, G., S. Kak and D. Frawley, 1995. *In Search of the Cradle of Civilization*. Wheaten: Quest Books.

Filliozat, J. 1970. The expansion of Indian medicine abroad. In Lokesh Chandra (ed.) *India's Contributions to World Thought and Culture*. Madras: Vivekananda Memorial Committee. 67-70.

Francfort, H.-P. 1992. Evidence for Harappan irrigation system in Haryana and Rajasthan. *Eastern Anthropologist*. vol. 45, 87-103.

Frawley, D. 1994. Planets in the Vedic literature. *Indian Journal of History of Science*. vol. 29, 495-506.

Kak, S. 1986. *The Nature of Physical Reality*. New York: Peter Lang.

—1987 The Pāṇinian approach to natural language processing. *Intl. Journal of Approximate Reasoning*, vol. 1, 117-130.

—1994a. *The Astronomical Code of the Ṛgveda*. New Delhi: Aditya.

—1994b. The evolution of writing in India. *Indian Journal of History of Science*. vol. 28, 375-388.

—1994c. *India at Century's End*. New Delhi: VOI.

—1995a. The astronomy of the age of geometric altars. *Quarterly Journal of the Royal Astronomical Society*. vol. 36, 385-396.

—1995b. From Vedic science to Vedanta. *The Adyar Library Bulletin*. vol. 59, 1-36.

—1996a. Knowledge of planets in the third millennium B.C. *Quarterly Journal of the Royal Astronomical Society*. vol. 37, 709-715.

—1996b. The three languages of the brain. In Pribram, K.H. and J. King (eds.) *Learning as Self-Organization*. Mahwah, NJ: Lawrence Erlbaum.

—1997a. *The rhythms of consciousness*. Quest. vol. 10, 52-56.

—I997b. Aspects of science in ancient India. In Sridhar, S. and N. Mattoo (eds.) *Ananya: A Portrait of India*. New York: AIA, 399-420.

—1997c. Archaeoastronomy and literature. Current Science. vol. 73, 624-627.

—1997d. On the science of consciousness in ancient India. *Indian Journal of History of Science*. vol. 32, 105-120.

Kennedy, K.A.R. 1995. Have Aryans been identified in the prehistoric skeletal record from South Asia? In Erdosy. G. (ed.). *The Indo-Aryans of South Asia*. Berlin: Walter de Gruyter, 32-66.

Lal, B.B. 1997. *The Earliest Civilization of South Asia*. New Delhi: Aryan International.

Matilal, B.K. 1968. *The Navva-Nyaya Doctrine of Negation*. Cambridge: Harvard University Press.

McClain. E.G. 1978. *The Myth of Invariance*. Boulder: Shambhala.

Sarma, K.V. 1985. A survey of source materials. *Indian Journal of History of Science*. vol. 20, 1-20.

Seidenberg, A. 1962. The ritual origin of geometry. *Archive for History of Exact Sciences*. vol. 1, 488-527.

—1978. The origin of mathematics. *Archive for History of Exact Sciences*. vol. 18, 301-342.

Selenius, C-O. 1975. Rationale of the chakravala process of Jayadeva and Bhaskara II. *Historia Mathematica*. vol. 2, 167-184.

Sengupta, P.C. 1947. *Ancient Indian Chronology*. Calcutta: University of Calcutta Press.

Shaffer, J. and D.L. Lichtenstein. 1995. The concept of "cultural tradition" and "paleoethnicity" in South Asian archaeology. In Erdosy, G. (ed.), *The Indo-Aryans of South Asia*. Berlin: Waiter de Gruyter, 126-154.

Staal, F. 1988. *Universals*. Chicago: University of Chicago Press.

van Nooten, B. 1993. Binary numbers in Indian antiquity. *Journal of Indian Philosophy*, vol. 21, 31-50.

Binary Numbers in Indian Antiquity*

B. van Nooten

Preliminary

Binary numbers have in recent time become indispensible for the workings of the digital computer since they allow the representation of any whole number in terms of two markers: "on" (1) and "off" (0). I have found good reason to believe that the rudiments of binary calculation were discovered in India well in advance of their discovery by the German philosopher Gottfried Leibniz in 1695.

Historians of Indian mathematics have for many decades recognized the contributions of the Indian mathematicians from as early as the time that the handbooks for constructing Vedic altars were composed (5th century B.C. ?). The better known contributions date from the period of the schools of Ujjain, Kusumapura and Mysore, from the fifth century A.D. until the eleventh. The discovery of the binary number may have escaped attention because its formulation is not contained in any of the strictly mathematical treatises of the Indian tradition [1]. Instead, I discovered it in an entirely different branch of science, the *chandaḥśāstra*, or "science of verse meters."

---

*Reprinted with kind permission from Kluwer Academic Publishers. Appeared previously in the Journal of Indian Studies 21: 31-50, 1993.

The Sanskrit Metrical Tradition

Piṅgala

The Vedic tradition ascribed a great, almost mystical significance to the meters of the sacrificial chants. Careful studies were made not only of the meters of the chant, but also of its language, prosody, proper place and proper time of recitation. The methodology developed to study and analyze meters became a respected field of study from a very early time onward. In this tradition the earliest comprehensive treatise on Vedic and Sanskrit meters that has been preserved is the *Chandaḥśāstra* by Piṅgala. Though most of the work is purely descriptive and is devoted to sorting out and classifying the meters according to their structure, in its eighth chapter occur a few brief statements that purport to establish a more general theory for dealing with the classification of meter. These statements or *sūtras* treat of the classification of metrical feet in a manner that suggests that Piṅgala was aware of the binary number. They have not been the subject of any special study in the West since the edition and translation of the *Chandaḥśāstra* by Albrecht Weber in 1863. They form the subject of this paper and I hope to show that in a devious and unexpected manner Piṅgala has succeeded in introducing the binary number as a means for classifying metrical patterns.

Piṅgala's *Chandaḥśāstra* fits into the literary genre of *sūtras*, or series of aphorismic statements that are memorized and serve as aides-de-memoire for a more complete theoretical exposition that is usually supplied by an explanatory commentary. The *Chandaḥśāstra* itself consists of some 310 brief sutras divided over eight books and it treats of the structure and nomenclature of meters. The main commentary on the *Chandaḥśāstra* is Halāyudha's

13th century *Mṛtasaṃjīvinī.* From an earlier date (8th century?) we have Kedāra's *Vṛttaratnākara*, an independent work based on Piṅgala, but dealing with non-vedic meters only.

The text-critical problems associated with the *Chandaḥśāstra* are similar to those of most ancient Indian literary works. We do not know who the author Piṅgala was, we do not know where he lived, when his work was composed and finally, whether the work going by his name was really all his, or a product of his school, or a conglomerate of text fragments assembled at one time and thenceforth transmitted under his name. Part of the evidence of its date is internal, part external. The text-critical work has been done almost exclusively by Albrecht Weber.

The main evidence for Piṅgala's date is external: his treatise is mentioned by the commentator Śabara on *Mimāṃsāsūtra* 1.1.5 who has been assigned to the 4th century A.D. [2]. The treatise as we have it now is probably a composite. However, the passage where the binary system is developed is to all likelihood part of the original work [3], and not an addition by a later metrist. The internal evidence of the treatise does not militate against a date before the 2nd century A.D. since the composition of the sutras follows the pattern of the older uncertified sutras, such as those contained in Pāṇini's *Aṣṭādhyāyī* [4]. It is not possible, on objective grounds to decide whether Piṅgala's treatise preceded or followed Pāṇini, nor is it possible to prove that Piṅgala's work existed before the third century A.D.

Piṅgala's Classification of Meters

A Sanskrit meter consists of verse feet which are composed of syllables which are prosodically either light (*laghu*) or heavy (*guru*). A light syllable (which I will represent as ∪), consists of a short vowel followed by at most one consonant and any other syllable is heavy (—). A verse meter usually consists of a set of four quarter verses (padas) with the same number of syllables each. The majority of Vedic verses have either 8-syllabic, or 11-syllabic, or 12-syllabic quarter verses. Within each quarter verse the succession of *laghu* and *guru* syllables varies within predictable limits. The metrist's task is to discover the parameters within which that variation takes place, to classify the meters and to organize them into larger categories.

The question may be raised why earlier Sanskritists and mathematicians have failed to pay attention to the binary theory of classification that Piṅgala proposed. The main reason is that this theory was one of two alternative solutions to the problem of the classification of meters. One solution, which will not be discussed here, is to divide each meter mechanically into units of three syllables then assign names to the meters on the basis of the combinations of triplets. This has become the accepted method of metrical analysis in India and has superseded every other classificational system that may have been devised earlier or later [5].

But in addition, Piṅgala experimented with another, less arbitrary and more universal means for inventorizing the meters, one that is of interest here. Instead of giving names to the meters he constructs a *prastāra*, a "bed" or matrix, in which the *laghus* and *gurus* are listed horizontally. Before I continue with the relevant passages from the Sanskrit texts, three remarks are in order:

a) Most of the metrists regard the value of the first and the last syllable of a verse line as indifferent to the definition of its meter. They can always be either short or long and are exempt from analysis. As a result, an eight-syllable verse is analyzed as if it had six syllables only.

b) The table they aim for starts with the number 1, not zero. This is of importance in the conversion of the binary number.

c) The Hindu scientific and arithmetical formulations, though precise and unambiguous, are at times difficult to translate without adding explanatory phrases.

Therefore, I have also translated remarks from the more explicit commentaries.

The device of the *prastāra* has to be visualized as an actual table written on a board, or in the dust on the ground [6]. Each horizontal line of the table stands for a line of verse represented as a succession of *laghu* and *guru* syllables. Every possible combination of *laghus* and *gurus* is spelled out for a particular meter. Hence there will be separate *prastāras* for 8-syllabic, for 11-syllabic and 12-syllabic meters. The first line in each will consist of all *laghus*, the last line of all *gurus*.

The two questions Piṅgala sets out to answer are:

a) Is it possible to give a numeric value to each line in a given *prastāra* so that we could give a unique value to every metrical quarter verse with a corresponding succession of *laghu* and *guru* syllables?

b) Suppose we are confronted with a verse meter in a text, how do we determine what the numeric value of that meter is?

Piṅgala is obviously not looking for an arbitrary numeration, such as counting the lines in the *prastāra* from top to bottom and assigning successive numbers. Instead, he produces mathematical formulas which define the position of the verse meter within the *prastāra* unambiguously. In the following paragraphs I have given the relevant Sanskrit text followed by its translation. The reason for being this explicit is that many of these texts have not been translated and some are rather difficult to locate. Piṅgala's own formulations are very brief.

Finding the Decimal Equivalent of a Metrical Pattern.

The rule for constructing the *prastāra* is given in ChŚ. 8.23 [7].

ekottarakramaśaḥ, purvapṛktā lasamkhyā

"In an order of one additional, the *la* is united with the previous one." The metrist Kedāra (8th century A.D.?) expands on this cryptic statement as follows:

a) pāde sarvagurāv ādyāl laghum nyasya guror adhah
b) yathopari tathā śeṣam bhūyah kuryād amum vidhim
c) ūne dadyād gurūn eva yāvat sarvalaghur bhavet
d) prastāro 'yam samākhyātaś chandovicitivedibhih

a) "In a line consisting entirely of gurus, starting from the beginning, having placed a laghu underneath a guru.
b) The rest remaining as (in the row) above, again and again one applies this rule.
c) One should place the gurus on one (place) less until the row) consists entirely of gurus.

d) This has been defined as a *prastāra* 'matrix' by the experts in *chandoviciti*, 'metric analysis'."

The rules for generating the *prastāra*, therefore, involve the following procedure:

One starts with writing down a row of *gurus* for as many syllables as the verse meter requires. For example, a four-syllabic verse will require:

— — — —

Next a new row of *gurus* is started, but underneath the first *guru* in the row above, a *laghu* is written instead. The remainder of the row remains unchanged:

— — — —
U — — —

On the next row again *gurus* are written until the first *guru* of the row above it is reached. Then a *laghu* is written. The remainder of the row remains unchanged:

— — — —
U — — —
— U — —

In the next row, again, a *laghu* is written underneath the first *guru* and the rest is copied.

— — — —
U — — —
— U — —
U U — —

And so the procedure continues:

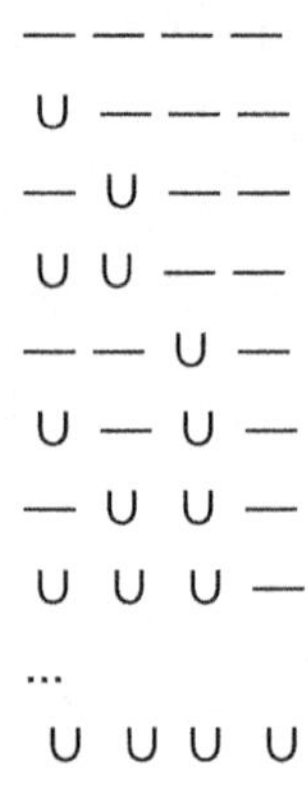

The last line consists entirely of laghus so that the rule will fail. Then the prastāra is complete.

Table I shows the complete prastāra for an eight-syllabic verse. As usual, its first and last syllables are ignored. Kedāra continues:

> *5ab) uddistam dvigunān aṅkān upary ādyāt samālikhet*
> *5cd) laghusthāne tu ye 'ṅkāh syus taih saikair miśritair bhavet*
> 5ab) "(Starting) from the beginning one should write numerals doubled above (the verse feet),
> 5cd) However, the numerals which would be above a short foot by those numerals combined together and augmented by one the (number of the meter) would be indicated."

	1. 2. 4. 8. 16. 32.		1. 2. 4. 8. 16. 32.		1. 2. 4. 8. 16. 32.		1. 2. 4. 8. 16. 32.
1.	— — — — — —	17.	— — — — U —	33.	— — — — — U	49.	— — — — U U
2.	U — — — — —	18.	U — — — U —	34.	U — — — — U	50.	U — — — U U
3.	— U — — — —	19.	— U — — U —	35.	— U — — — U	51.	— U — — U U
4.	U U — — — —	20.	U U — — U —	36.	U U — — — U	52.	U U — — U U
5.	— — U — — —	21.	— — U — U —	37.	— — U — — U	53.	— — U — U U
6.	U — U — — —	22.	U — U — U —	38.	U — U — — U	54.	U — U — U U
7.	— U U — — —	23.	— U U — U —	39.	— U U — — U	55.	— U U — U U
8.	U U U — — —	24.	U U U — U —	40.	U U U — — U	56.	U U U — U U
9.	— — — U — —	25.	— — — U U —	41.	— — — U — U	57.	— — — U U U
10.	U — — U — —	26.	U — — U U —	42.	U — — U — U	58.	U — — U U U
11.	— U — U — —	27.	— U — U U —	43.	— U — U — U	59.	— U — U U U
12.	U U — U — —	28.	U U — U U —	44.	U U — U — U	60.	U U — U U U
13.	— — U U — —	29.	— — U U U —	45.	— — U U — U	61.	— — U U U U
14.	U — U U — —	30.	U — U U U —	46.	U — U U — U	62.	U — U U U U
15.	— U U U — —	31.	— U U U U —	47.	— U U U — U	63.	— U U U U U
16.	U U U U — —	32.	U U U U U —	48.	U U U U — U	64.	U U U U U U

Table 1: The Prastāra of six syllables

We find a fuller explanation of this statement in a subcommentary, the Tātparyatīkā of the commentator Trivikrama (12th century): [8]

"tatrā 'yam udāharaṇapradarśanāyā 'lapah: ⍰ ⍰ — ⍰ — ⍰ ⍰ —; idam vyaktisvarupam anustubhi jātau kathitam bhavatī 'ti ukte idam īdṛśam eve ksitau praviralam dhriyate. tasmād upari dvigunān ādyād upary aṅkān samālikhet iti vacanāt pratyaksaram kramena ekasmād ārabhya dvigunān aṅkān samālikhed, yathā:"

"Here is a formula to show an example: U U — U — U U —. If the question is raised: 'What number does this particular pattern in the anustubh class (of meters) have ?, this very same (pattern) is retained separately on the board. Next, because of the statement that one should write doubled figures above it, one writes numbers as follows, one after the other, beginning with one, syllable by syllable:

1 2 4 8 16 32 64 128"
U U — U — U U —

Trivikrama continues:

"tatrā 'ṅkāh taih saikair miśritair bhavet iti vacanād etad vyaktau laghustham ekam dvāv aṣṭau dvātriṃśac catuhṣaṣṭim ca samgrhnīyāt, tatraikam dhruvakarūpam ca ksipet. etasmin miśrena jāto rāśih 108."

"Next, since it is stated that the numerals above a *laghu* in the scheme have to be combined and augmented by one, we would get: one, two, eight, thirty-two, sixty-four. Then we should add one to the sum obtained. In this (case) through the combination is obtained the value 108."

1+2 + 8 + 32 + 64 = 107. Add one: 108
U U — U — U U —

So the rank number of the metrical line in the *prastāra* is 108.

Through this procedure the metrical line is interpreted as a number. Each syllable is assigned a numerical value based on its position in the meter. The first syllable has the value 1 and each subsequent syllable has a positional value twice that of its left neighbor. In effect, this scheme is exactly equivalent to a system of numerical notation where the positional values of the digits increase as the powers of 2, from 2^0 to 2^n, which we call the binary notation. The difference between Piṅgala's system and the one current in the West is that the Indian system placed the higher positional value to the right of the lower, whereas in the West we find the lowest value on the right. The *laghu* in Piṅgala's system serves to indicate that the position in the number is significant, the equivalent of our notation 1. The *guru* means that the position is ignored, our 0. The Western representation of this number would be: 1 1 0 1 0 1 1.

In this way Piṅgala has shown that a metrical pattern can be regarded as a binary number. As a further illustration, let us find the rank number of an eight-syllabic Vedic gayatri verse:

tat savitur vareṇiaṃ

whose metrical representation is:

U̲ U U — U — U U̲

We list the six central syllables in a vertical column (1) and start a new column (2) where each *laghu* is given the value 1 and each *guru* is left without a numerical value. Column (3) begins with 1 and the subsequent numbers are the doubled value of the preceding number. Next, in column (4), the values in column (2) are multiplied with those in column (3):

The numbers in column (4) are added up and the total, 43, is the decimal value of the binary number represented in column (2). To get the rank number of the metrical pattern in the prastāra we add 1 to the total: 43 + 1 = 44.

(1)	(2)	(3)	(4)
verse foot	numercical value	binary base	product (2) × (3)
∪ laghu	1	1	1
∪ laghu	1	2	2
— guru		4	
∪ laghu	1	8	8
—guru		16	
∪ laghu	1	32	32

Next, the converse process, that of determining the binary equivalent of a decimal number is given.

Finding the Binary Equivalent of a Decimal Number

The process of converting a decimal number to a binary number is formulated as one of finding the metrical pattern if one knows its (decimal) rank number and the metrical representation has been "destroyed" (naṣṭa), presumably a reference to the short persistence of a diagram written in the sand.

Piṅgala, (Ch. Ś. 8.24-25): [9]

1 ardhe, saike *g*

"A *laghu* in case of a half: in the case of an additional 1, a *guru*"

Halāyudha explaining Piṅgala states:

1 ardhe

yadai 'vam vijijñāset gāyatryām samavṛttam ṣaṣṭham kidṛśam, iti tadā tam eva satsankhyāviśeṣam ardhayeta. tasminn ardhikṛte laghur eko lakṣyate, sa bhūmau vinyāsyah. idānim avaśiṣṭā trisankhyāvisamatvād ardhayitum na śakyate. tatra kim pratipattavyam ity āha:

saike g

tam pūrvalabdhāl lakārāt param sthāpayet. tato dvisankhyā 'vaśiṣyate. punas tām ardhayeta tataś cai 'kalakāram dadyāt tataś cai 'kasankhyā 'vaśiṣyate. tatra tāvat sai 'ke g iti laksanam āvartanīyam yāvad vṛttāksarāni sat pūryante. evam sankhyāntare 'pi yojyam.

"If (the metrist) is concerned to determine which pattern in the six-syllable *gāyatrī*, for instance, is the sixth, provided all are of the same length, then that numeral six should be halved. When this has been halved, one obtains one laghu which is written separately on the ground (bhumau). Now, since the remaining number three, because of its odd-ness cannot be halved, how should one proceed?" (Quotes:) "A *laghu* in case of a half; in the case of an additional 1, a *guru*."

'To the odd number he adds a 1 and halves again. In this way he gets a single *guru* which he places beside the *laghu*. The remaining three are halved again and he gets a *guru*. To the remaining 1 he adds a 1, gets a *guru*, which he places beside the *laghu* he got earlier. So the number 2 remains. He halves that again and adds another *laghu*. This continues until the six-syllable gayatri is full. In the same way one can proceed with any other number."

The procedure outlined here involves a series of divisions by 2 of the rank number of the meter. It speaks for itself: the initial number is halved and if the quotient is an even number, a laghu is written in a separate table. If the quotient is an odd number, a guru is written in the same separate table, one is added to the quotient and the halving continues.

To give an example, if the decimal number one has is 54 and one wishes to find the metrical pattern that represents it, one proceeds as follows:

Write: 54	Write:
divide by 2, -> 27:	*laghu*
add 1, divide by 2, -> 14:	*guru*
divide by 2, -> 7	*laghu*
add 1, divide by 2, ->4:	*guru*
divide by 2, -> 2	*laghu*
divide by 2, -> 1	*laghu*

The last column reads from top to, bottom:

laghu guru laghu guru laghu laghu, or:
U — U — U U

A glance at the earlier described *prastāra* (Table 1) shows that, indeed, the metrical pattern we have obtained is no. 54. In this way Piṅgala solves the problem of reconstructing a metrical pattern if only the rank number is known. The procedure is equivalent to that of finding the binary representation of a decimal number.

Historical Importance

The importance of Piṅgala's discovery is twofold: it implies that he was aware of a place-value system of numerical notation and it also shows that he was working with a numerical base other than base 10. In the following paragraphs I propose to determine whether Piṅgala's discovery sprang from a known tradition, or whether he was the originator of his theory.

Piṅgala's notation represents two separate historical developments of numerical systems: that of the place-value system of numeration and that of the recognition of numerical systems not based on powers of ten. Ifrah [10] adduces evidence that four world civilizations have invented a place-value system: the Babylonians, the Indians, the Chinese with their rod numerals and entirely independently, the Mayans of the New World [11]. Was India influenced by the other Old-World cultures?

The Babylonian place value system was sexagesimal, or based on the number 60. Its influence on India is found in the later astronomical works, but not in early India. The Chinese discovered a good decimal place value system during the Han Dynasty (3rd century B.C.) [12]. Yet there is no evidence to show that the Indians knew of this system.

Within India itself evidence for systems of numbering and counting can come from two sources: one, the counting system of the language itself and two, the representation of numbers by numerals. We shall now briefly examine the evidence about the ancient Indian counting system by looking at the sources: the ancient Indic languages, the older literature and the inscriptions.

Sanskrit, being an Indo-European language, has inherited a system of counting in tens. The numbers from 1 through 10 have arbitrary names, but the numeration continues systematically by tens from twenty through ninety. The word for "ten" in the enumeration of numerals is followed by expressions for 10 + 1, 10 + 2, etc. The numerals

20, 30, etc. are variations on a compound *śati+*, or *ṭi+*. The hundreds again are based on a new name, *śatam*, and so are thousands and one hundred thousand. The counting system of a language tends to influence the manner in which numbers are written [13]. At Piṅgala's time the prevailing language was Sanskrit or one of its derivatives and so people counted in tens.

History in India begins with the Vedic civilization where in the Taittirīya Saṃhitā of the Black Yajurveda (1000 B.C.) we have the first written indication of a numeration system based on the 10. Different ways of counting are presented, not with figures, but with the names of the numbers:

> "thousand... ten thousand, one hundred thousand, ten hundred thousand, ten million, one hundred million, ten thousand million, one hundred thousand million, ten hundred thousand million."
>
> (TS. vii.2.19-20, Keith 1914)

The assumption underlying the decimal notation is that reading from left to right, within a decimal number each digit represents a value equal to one-tenth of its left neighbor. This process is first formally defined by the mathematician Āryabhaṭa I (b. 476 A.D.) who writes that "the value of a place (of a number) is ten times that of the (preceding) place: (*sthānāt sthānam daśaguṇam syāt*)" [14]. Later still, in approximately the 7th century A.D., we find this principle repeated in a different form in Vyāsa's commentary on Patañjali's Yogasūtra no. 3.13: "*yathai' kā rekhā śatasthāne śatam daśasthāne daśai kā cai 'kasthāne*" "...just as one and the same numeral (rekha) in the 100-position is 100, in the 10-position is ten and is 1 in the 1-position" [15]. Though these remarks postdate Piṅgala's presumed date, they are not ever contradicted by statements in the literature that imply that a non-decimal place value system was in use.

The Indian writing system again supports the decimal place value system. From a few centuries before Piṅgala's time we have numerals contained in the inscriptions of Nāneghāṭ on the western scarp of the Deccan Plateau, north and east of Bombay. They belong to the *Brāhmī* alphabet which is written from left to right (see Fig. 1). In these numbers the digit with the highest value is written on the left, and the lowest number to its right, e.g. 12 is written as 10 2, or O = = and 17 as O = ? [16]. The numeral is often, but not necessarily, preceded by words spelling out the number. From the fact that independent symbols existed for "10", "20", "80", "100", etc. we can infer that the counting system underlying these numerals was founded on a decimal base. Of course, it is not a pure place-value system because in such a system there would be no need for designing separate symbols for 10, 50, 100, etc. None of the numerals suggest that another system, such as a duodecimal or sexagesimal was in use. The same is true for all the subsequent numbers of dates in Indian history. To our knowledge, Piṅgala was not exposed to a tradition of marking numerals in a base other than 10 [17].

To summarize the evidence for the state of mathematics in Piṅgala's time, we can be reasonably certain that his counting system was predicated on a base of ten, but there is no proof that the place-value system of notation was used. Piṅgala's *Chandaḥśāstra* itself does not provide us with representations of numerals. The manuscripts of the commentaries do write them, but these postdate the invention of the zero. Although the word for "zero" (*śūnya*) does occur in the *Chandaḥśāstra*, it is always spelled out and not represented by a symbol.

Numerals.	Their Value.	Numerals.	Their Value.
[illegible]	12	—	1
—	1	[illegible]	12
[illegible]	1700	[illegible]	21,000
[illegible]	189	—	1
[illegible]	17	[illegible]	60,000
[illegible]	11,000	[illegible]	10,001
[illegible]	1,000	[illegible]	101
[illegible]	12	[illegible]	1,100
—	1	[illegible]	100
[illegible]	24,400	[illegible]	101
[illegible]	6,000	[illegible]	1,101
—	1	[illegible]	1,101
—	1	[illegible]	101
[illegible]	1	[illegible]	1002
[illegible]	100	[illegible]	1,001

Figure 1: Indian numerals from Piṅgala's time (Naneghat, ca. 1st century B.C.)

It remains for us to determine in how far the procedures that Piṅgala prescribed for converting a verse meter into a decimal number, and vice versa, are equivalent to those required to convert a binary number into a decimal number. A system of notation that simply uses "Off" and "On", or "+" and "-" as markers of a place value does not necessarily produce a binary system. In fact, you have no more than people who count up to two have. But if we have a system that uses two symbols "+" and "-" in such a way that every string of "+"s and "-"s has a unique decimal equivalent and we are shown how to derive this decimal equivalent and also how to convert any decimal number into a string of "+"s and "-"s with a unique numerical value, then indeed we do have a binary system. Piṅgala has done at least this much and as I will show next, his representation of numbers as members of a *prastāra* bears close comparison with the method Leibniz followed in his discovery of the binary number.

Europe and India

The discovery of the binary notation of numbers in Europe was the work of the German philosopher Gottfried Leibniz (1646-1716) at the end of the 17th century [18]. In a letter which spells out the first description of his discovery, he writes:

> "... ich sehe, dass sich aus dieser Schreibart der Zahlen wunderliche Vorteil ergeben (werden), die hernach auch in der gemeinen Rechnung zu statten kommen warden..." [19]

The hastily sketched table (Fig. 2) makes it clear how he derived the values of binary numbers. He writes 15 rows each beginning with a 1. In each subsequent row he writes an additional "0" after the "1". To the right of the last column of each line he draws a vertical line and to the right of this line writes a column of numbers 1 2 4 8, etc. Each of these numbers corresponds to the binary value represented by the preceding row of "1"'s and "0"'s.

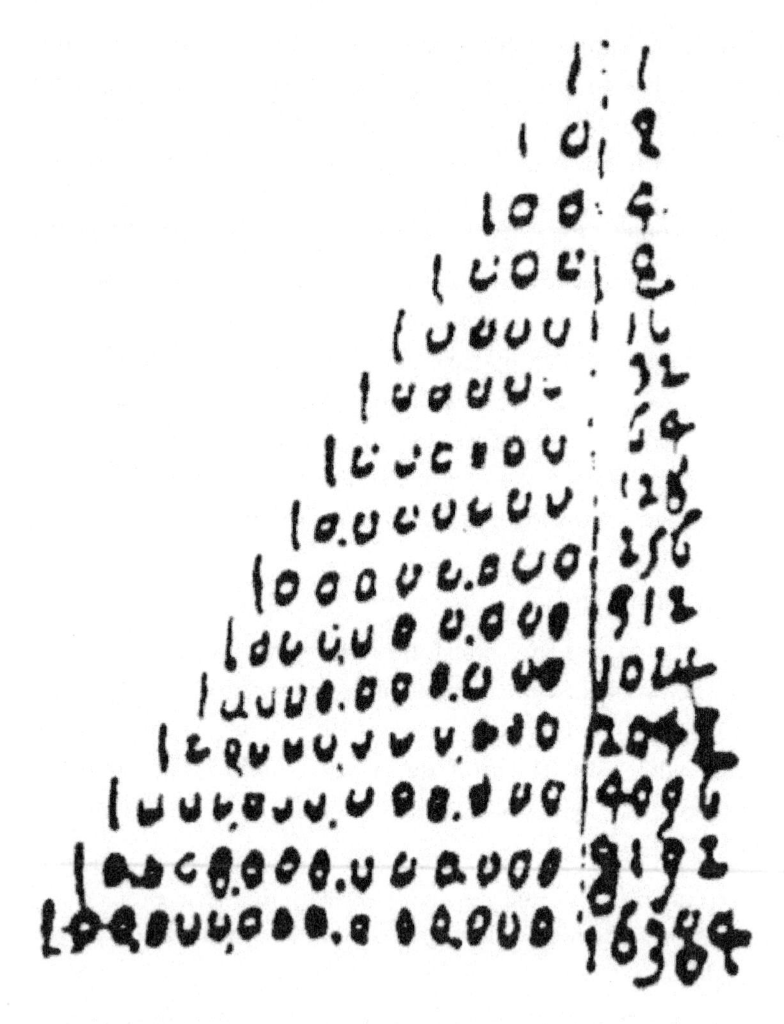

Figure 2. Leibniz's diagram of Binary Numbers. (Couturat 1903 p. 284)

This table can be reconciled with the *prastāra* model as follows: The column of powers of 2 in both diagrams are exactly equivalent, but the rank numbers given to the metrical patterns are systematically one more than their binary equivalents. Piṅgala's *prastāra* for 6 syllables (Table

1) ends with the pattern U U U U U U, binary 63, to which the metrist assigns the number 64. It is one short of Leibniz's 7-digit binary number 1000000, before 64 in his table. The pattern (— — — — — — U), which would conform exactly to Leibniz's 1000000, would be the next entry, # 65 starting a 7-syllable *prastāra*. The difference in numbering is due to the fact that the rank numbers in a prastāra are shifted up one decimal value.

To find an explanation for this difference we can speculate that the metrist may have added the value of 1 to the value of the binary number, because of practical considerations. He may have been reluctant to assign the rank number 0 to the first pattern in a *prastāra*, because it runs counter to the intuitive method of counting. The metrical *prastāra* obviously had a very practical purpose, that of classifying meters, and so we should regard this *prasrara* procedure as the practical application of a more general mathematical theory of binary numerals, to the science of metrics. Further evidence in support of this supposition is the fact that in some of the theoretical expositions the first and last syllables of the meter are not ignored (see Trivikrama on Kedāra 2.238, above p.7). These expositions, in other words, treat of the metrical pattern of a verse as an abstract unit of calculation, while the practical metrists leave the first and last syllables out of consideration. The first and last syllables have no practical value for the classification of meters and their inclusion would unnecessarily have increased the number of lines in a *prastāra*.

The most striking difference between Leibniz's system and Piṅgala's is the order in which the powers of 2 are arranged. In the binary number of Leibniz's design the low digit is on the right, the high value on the left. It is the precursor of the Western system of binary notation. In Piṅgala's arrangement (Table 1) the lowest value is on the left. This fundamental difference is primary evidence of the originality of both discoveries.

Leibniz's letter referred to above is, indeed, the earliest published account of his discovery. However, Leibniz's notes from 20 years earlier (1677-78) contain a fragment which shows that already at that time he was experimenting with the binary notation which he calls "*Progressio Dyadico*", or "Characteristica bimalis":

> *"...perfectior est characteristica numerorum bimalis quam decimalis, vel alia quaecunque...". [20]*

I mention this fragment, for several years later Leibniz became intrigued with the Chinese hexagram depictions of Fu Hsi (Fohy) in the *Book of Changes (I Ching)* which he interpreted as binary numbers (Fig.3).

The letter where he expresses this opinion is included in Loosen-Vonessen 1968 pp. 126-131. The fragment quoted earlier makes it obvious that he had discovered the binary number prior to learning of the Chinese text. In fact, however, the *I Ching,* unlike Piṅgala, does not contain evidence for the use of the binary number. Chinese culture was the great discovery of the Enlightenment and so Leibniz looked there for expressions of rational thought and not to India which might have had more to offer. Sanskrit texts were simply unavailable to scholars of the 17th century. India was the discovery of the Romantic Period and became, for better or worse, identified as the land of religion. Since Leibniz could not have known Piṅgala's work we have another instance here of a Western rediscovery of a mathematical principle, this time one millennium and a half later.

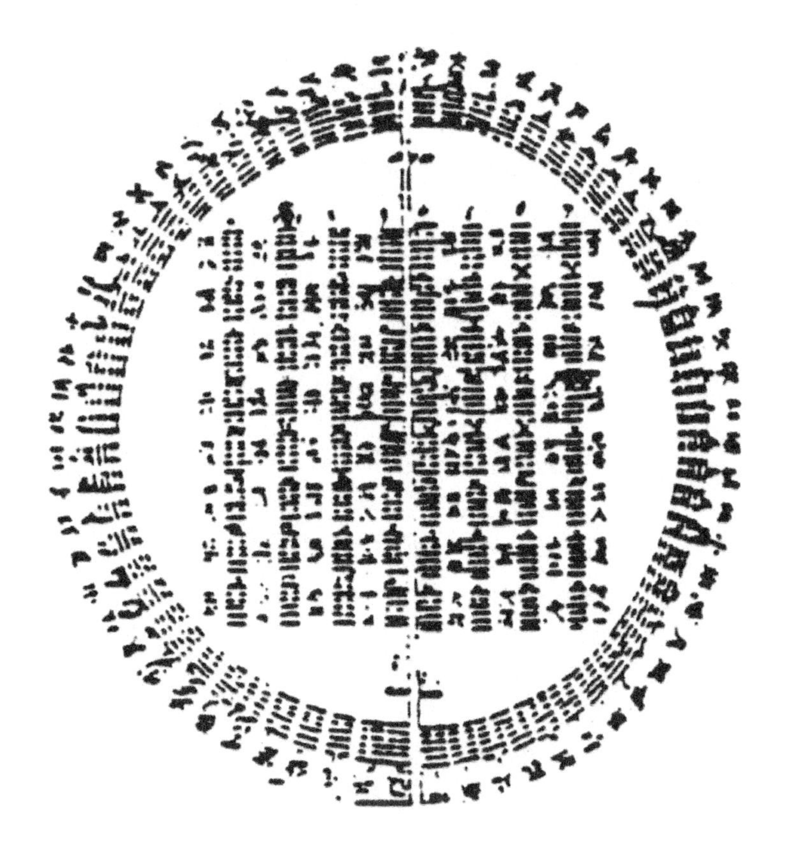

Fig. 3. The "Prior to Heaven Hexagram Order," Hsien-tien tzu-hsu (D.E. Mungeilo: 1977, Leibniz and Confucianism, the search for accord, p. 52).

In summary, I have tried to show that Piṅgala used a binary notation to classify metrical verses as early as the second or third century A.D. He also knew how to convert that binary notation to a decimal notation and vice versa. We know of no sources from which he could have drawn his inspiration, so he may well have been the originator of the system. Piṅgala leaves no record of further applications of his discovery, but it is of great interest to realize that for many centuries, down to the present time, in fact, this knowledge was available to and preserved by Sanskrit students of metrics. Unlike the case of the great linguistic discoveries of the Indians which directly influenced and inspired Western linguistics, this discovery of the theory of binary numbers has so far gone unrecorded in the annals of the West [21].

References

Apte, V. S. 1959. *The Practical Sanskrit-English Dictionary*. 3 vols. Poona: Prasad Prakashan.

Bag, A. K. 1979. *Mathematics in Ancient and Medieval India*. Varanasi: Chaukhambha Orientalia.

Bharati, Sri Ramacandra, ed. 1908. *Vṛttaratnākara by Pandit Kedārabhaṭṭa, with its Commentary Vṛttaratnākarapañcikā*. Bombay: Nirnaya-Sagar Press.

Bodas, Rajaram Shastri, ed. 1917. *The Yogasūtras of Patañjali with the Scholium of Vyāsa*. Bombay Sanskrit and Prakrit Series No. XLVI. Bombay: Government Central Press: 131-132.

Bühler, J. Georg. 1904. "Indian Paleography", (trl. from the German by J. F. Fleet). *Indian Antiquary* 33. Appendix.: 1-102.

Closs. Michael P. 1986. *Native American Mathematics*. Austin: University of Texas Press.

Couturat, Louis. ed. 1903. Opuscules et fragments inédits de Leibniz, extraits des manuscrits de la Bibliotheque royale de Hanovre par Louis Couturat ... Paris: Alcan.

Datta, Bibhutibhusan and Avadesh N. Singh. 1935. *History of Indian Mathematics*. 2 vols; repr. 1 vol. 1962. Bombay: Asian Publishing House.

Gokhale, Sh. L. 1966. *Indian Numerals*. Poona: Deccan College Silver Jubilee Series No. 43. Chart nos. 4, 6, 14, 20.

Ifrah, Georges. 1985. *From One to Zero*. New York: Viking Penguin Inc.

Indraji, Bhagavanlal. 1876. "On Ancient Nagari Numeration; from an Inscription at Naneghat". *Journal of the Bombay Branch of the Royal Asiatic Society* 12: 404-406.

Jacobi, Hermann. 1933. "Uber die ältesten indischen Metriker und ihr Werk." *Indian Linguistics: Grierson Comm. Volume*. Lahore: 131- 141.

Keith, Arthur Berriedale. 1914. *The Veda of the Black Yajus School*. Cambridge: Harvard Oriental Series 19 Part II: 350-351.

Loosen, Renate and Franz Vonessen, ed. 1968. *Gottfried Wilhelm Leibniz. Zwei Briefe über das Binäre Zahlensystem und die Chinesische Philosophie*. Stuttgart: Belser-Presse.

Seidenberg, A. 1986. "The Zero in the Mayan Numerical Notation," in *Michael Closs* 1986, pp. 371-386.

Shankar, Kripa, ed., trans. 1976. *Aryabhatiya of Aryabhata*. New Delhi: the Indian National Science Academy.

Sharma, Aryendra, K. Deshpande and D. G. Padhye, ed. 1969. *Vṛttaratnākara of Śrī Kedāra Bhaṭṭa*. Hyderabad: Osmania University.

Sircar, D. C. 1965. *Indian Epigraphy*. Delhi: Motilal Banarsidass.

Velankar, H.D. (1949). *Kedāraviracito Vṛttaratnākaraḥ in Jayadaman*. Bombay: Haritosha Samiti.

Weber, Albrecht. 1863. Über die Metrik der Inder. *Indische Studien* No. 8. Berlin.

Woods, James H., trans. 1914. The Yoga-system of Patañjali, Cambridge: *Harvard Oriental Series* 17.

Notes

1. See for instance, H.L. Resnikoff and R.O. Wall, Mathematics in Civilization, Dover Publ. 1984 (2nd Ed.), who correctly credits the Babylonians with inventing the place-value system of numerals, but is silent about the Indian contributions, The Āryabhaṭiya, in fact does have a chapter on metrics, but it confines itself to the theory of permutations.
2. Śabara was known to the astronomer Varāhamihira whose date we know fairly accurately. The date of 200 B.C. that Datta and Singh 1935 p.75 assign to Piṅgala is puzzling. They do not justify the date, nor quote authorities confirming it.
3. Jacobi (1933) is of this opinion ("...zweifellos echt" p. 138) pointing out that discussions of the *prastāra* are found also in the *Bharatanāṭyam* XIV (appr. 4th century A.D.) and agreements can be found with earlier passages in Piṅgala's work. The passage preceding it (VIII.2-19) is absent from all the Ṛg-recensions of the *Piṅgalaśāstra* and from many of the Yajus manuscripts and is therefore, suspect (Weber 1863 p 414).
4. We recognize the use of *adhikāras* such as "*chandas*" (1.1), the *anuvṛttis*, the use of "sese" (2.12) to include unnamed contexts, the use of the ablative to indicate context-after and the locative for the context-before. In brief, enough similarities exist to show that the descriptive techniques used by Piṅgala and the grammarians were similar.
5. The theory of analysis of meter by ganas can be found in Weber 1863 and in Appendix A to Apie 1959, Vol. iii, after p. 1755.

6. One of the names of mathematics in ancient India was "Science of Dust", since figures and diagrams were drawn in the sand.
7. Weber 1863 p 429; *Vṛttaratnākara* 6.2; Bharati 1908 p 90; Sharma et al. P. 306.
8. Sharma et al. pp. 306ff.
9. *Chandaḥśāstra* p. 192.
10. Ifrah 1985. chapters 26-27.
11. Seidenberg 1986.
12. Ifrah 1985, p.398.
13. This correspondence is not necessary and not always observed. The Jains for instance, have a separate numeral for 400, but no special name for it. Conversely, many different terms can be used to express the values of the first nine numerals of Sanskrit. See Sircar 1965 pp. 247-248.
14. *Āryabhaṭiya Gaṇita*, vs. 2. Shankar 1976.
15. *Yogasūtra* pp. 131-132 and Woods 1913 pp. 215-216.
16. See Bhagavanlal Indraji 1876. pp. 404-406.
17. The location of this inscription on a monument at the head of a mountain pass on a busy trade route connecting the Arabian Sea to the Indian hinterland area, may well indicate that the system of notation was similar to a system adopted by traders and merchants. These traders were likely to have used an abacus for their calculations which may have played a role in spreading the decimal system. (Bühler Indian Palaeography §35B). The oldest abacus, or calculating board known to us was invented in China during the Han dynasty (Ifrah op.cit. pp-118-119), or between 206 B.C. and A.D. 221. In the later period of this dynasty Buddhist monks began to travel from China to India, so that the presence of an abacus in Naneghat at that time should not surprise us.

However, there is no clear proof of the use of an abacus in India from this early a period.

18. My thanks are to Professor Benson Mates of the Department of Philosophy, Berkeley, for referring me to the relevant passages of Leibniz.
19. Loosen-Vonessen 1968, p. 23.
20. Couturat 1903, p. 284.
21. I thank Professor J. F. Staal, Professor of Philosophy and Sanskrit, University of California, Berkeley, for his very helpful crooners on the final draft of this paper.

The Katapayadi Formula and the Modern Hashing Technique†

Anand V. Raman

The essence of the modern hashing technique in computer science is the derivation of a number from a nonnumeric key to index into a table where the record containing the key is stored. In this paper, an interestingly similar technique used in South Indian musicology in the 18th century is described, and the question of whether it is an anticipation of the hashing technique is briefly addressed.

The problem of retrieving a record from a table based upon a given key has been studied extensively [1]. In this paper, I describe one particular approach to this problem—hashing—and also an interesting earlier development very similar to it. It is generally believed that the idea of hashing was originated by H. P. Luhn, in an internal IBM memorandum in 1953 [2], and first described in the open literature by Arnold Dumey [3]. But is it possible that the Katapayadi scheme of deriving numbers from names—in conjunction with the applications to which it had been put, especially in classical South Indian musicology—is an early anticipation of the hashing technique? I will discuss this issue in more detail here.

Hashing

A hash table is a data structure in which it takes, on average, a constant time to find any given element. This constant time is the time taken to compute a function, called the hash function, of the element being sought. This is in contrast to a binary search tree data structure, for example, in which the time taken to find an element is, on average, proportional to the $\log_2 N$, an array or linked linear list data structure in which the time is proportional to N, where N is the total number of elements. The following example illustrates the use of hashing, where the marks of 10 students need to be stored in a table. It is a trivial example, but it is sufficient to bring out the essential principle behind hashing.

Example

Examination marks for 10 students (Aaron, Bean, Chang, Diana. Emma, Fred, Guru, Hoyle, Ingrid, and James) need to be stored in a table. We might additionally want to retrieve the mark of a student on demand and, optionally, modify it. One way of doing this is to store the marks sequentially in a table of size 10 and perform a sequential search on it each time we want to retrieve a particular record. This would mean that, on average, we can expect to scan half the table (five elements) before finding the desired record. A more efficient storage technique would be to store the elements in order sorted by name. In this case, we would expect to search the table $\log_2 10$ (approximately 3.2) times, on average, for each retrieval, because at each examination, our search space is effectively halved, as the element we want is either current, in the upper half or lower half, depending on whether it is equal to, less than, or greater than the current element.

In contrast to these techniques, the hashing scheme derives a unique number corresponding to each name, which gives us the cell address of the element in the table. If we used a hash function H(x) = (ascii(x[0]) - 5) % 10+1, where x is the name or value being hashed, x[0] is the first letter of that name, ascii0 is a function that returns the ASCII value of a given letter, and % stands for the modulus or remainder operator, then the arrangement of elements in Table 1 would be seen.

Table 1. Hash Function for 10 Names

Addr	0	1	2	3	4
Name	Adrian	Bean	Chang	Diana	Emma
Mark					
Addr	5	6	7	8	9
Name	Fred	Guru	Hoyle	Ingrid	James
Mark					

To retrieve an element, we would not have to scan any part of the table, but could go directly to the record's location by computing its hash value. For example, if Emma wants to know what her mark was, since ascii("E") = 69, we compute (69 - 5) % 10, which gives four, the location of Emma's record in Table 1.

Of course, there are other important considerations, such as the number of elements that can be stored at any given table location (called a bucket) and how to accommodate overflows and handle collisions (two or more elements with the same hash value). It has been pointed out to me by a reviewer of this paper that such considerations are as important as the derivation of the index. But, it can be argued that these are secondary in nature, given the motivation of the hashing technique. Its essence can be said to be the derivation of a number from a given key, which is then subsequently used to index into an array where the element is stored with the purpose of eliminating a scan of any part of the array.

The Katapayadi Scheme

In classical India, letters of the Sanskrit alphabet were initially used to represent numbers. The grammarian Pāṇini (fourth or fifth century BC), who is believed to have written the first generative grammar for a natural language [4], assigned the values one through nine and zero to the Sanskrit vowels a, i, u, etc. For example, *Sūtra* (rule) v.i.30 of his grammar, *Aṣṭādhyāyī*, is marked with the letter i, which indicates that the rule applies to the next two rules [5]. It is also known that various synonyms for the number words existed. In one system, words with meanings evocative of the numbers they represented were used. For example, the words *indu* (moon) and *dharā* (earth) stood for the number one, since there was only one of each, *netra* (eyes) and *pakṣa* (wings) stood for two, and so on. A more comprehensive list of such synonyms can be found in the work by Ifrah [6], who also gives the following instance of its use by Bhaskara I, who in 629 AD wrote the number 4,320,000 as *viyatambarākāśaśūnyayamarāmaveda*, or sky/atmosphere/space/void/primordial couple/Rama/Veda= 0000234.

The Katapayadi scheme was initially just another such system of expressing numbers through the use of letters (Sanskrit consonants in this case), with more than one synonym for each number. The consonants themselves were unevocative of the values they represented, unlike the earlier scheme, but they now possessed the powerful ability to form easily memorizable words through the insertion of vowels between them. Meaningful and mnemonic words could now be formed using these letters in much the same way as mnemonic words are coined today to represent commercial telephone numbers. In this sense, the Katapayadi scheme could be seen as just a mnemonic technique to help remember numbers or, at best, a coding scheme like ASCII to derive numeric values from nonnumeric tokens, but it is noteworthy that the scheme continued to be used long after the invention of numeric symbols and, during this time, was put to several applications. It is the application of the scheme to the particular instance described in the next section that is remarkably similar to that of modern hashing.

The verse shown in Fig. 1 (transliterated from Sanskrit using the International Phonetic Alphabet) describes one version of the Katapayadi scheme. J.F. Fleet [7] quotes this from C.M. Whish [8] who quotes this from an unspecified source, but B. Datta and A.N. Singh [5] state that it is found in *Sadratnamālā*, which is a treatise on astronomy published in 1823 by Prince Sankaravarman of Katattanat in North Malabar, India. The prince was an acquaintance of Whish's, who spoke of him in high terms as "a very intelligent man and acute mathematician" [9]. *Sadratnamālā* was published with a commentary in the Malayalam-language monthly Kavanodayam (vol. 16, 1898).

ñ and n denote zeros; the letters (in succession) beginning with k, ṭ, p and y denote the digits. In a conjoint consonant, only the last one denotes a number; and a consonant not joined to a vowel should be disregarded. There are said to be four variations of this scheme, which is claimed as the reason for its not coming into general use.

nañavacaśca śunyani samkhya kaṭapayādayaḥ
miśre tūpānta hal samkhya na ca cintyo halasvaraḥ

Fig. 1. Verse describing one version of the Katapayadi scheme.

The transcription scheme is more easily understood from Fig. 2. It lists the Sanskrit consonants with their associated numeric values as specified in the verse. Each of the lines except the last consists of stops in the following sequence: unvoiced and unaspirated, unvoiced and aspirated, voiced and unaspirated, voiced and aspirated, and nasal. In the first line, the velars are followed by the palatals; in the second line, the retroflexes are followed by the dentals. The last line consists of fricatives.

The interesting verse shown in Fig. 3, also appearing in *Sadratnamala,* illustrates an application of the scheme.

If we translate the verse from Fig. 3 using the procedure described earlier in the verse about the scheme, we get

bh = 4 (from table)

<table>
<tr><td rowspan="4">Velar & Palatal Stops</td><td>1</td><td>2</td><td>3</td><td>4</td><td>5</td></tr>
<tr><td>k</td><td>kh</td><td>g</td><td>gh</td><td>ṅ</td></tr>
<tr><td>6</td><td>7</td><td>8</td><td>9</td><td>0</td></tr>
<tr><td>c</td><td>ch</td><td>j</td><td>jh</td><td>ñ</td></tr>
<tr><td rowspan="4">Retroflex and Dental Stops</td><td>1</td><td>2</td><td>3</td><td>4</td><td>5</td></tr>
<tr><td>ṭ</td><td>ṭ h</td><td>ḍ</td><td>ḍ h</td><td>ṇ</td></tr>
<tr><td>6</td><td>7</td><td>8</td><td>9</td><td>0</td></tr>
<tr><td>t</td><td>th</td><td>d</td><td>dh</td><td>n</td></tr>
<tr><td rowspan="2">Labial Stops</td><td>1</td><td>2</td><td>3</td><td>4</td><td>5</td></tr>
<tr><td>p</td><td>ph</td><td>b</td><td>bh</td><td>m</td></tr>
<tr><td rowspan="4">Fricatives</td><td>1</td><td>2</td><td>3</td><td>4</td><td>5</td></tr>
<tr><td>y</td><td>r</td><td>l</td><td>v</td><td>ś</td></tr>
<tr><td>6</td><td>7</td><td>8</td><td>9</td><td>0</td></tr>
<tr><td>ṣ</td><td>s</td><td>h</td><td></td><td></td></tr>
</table>

Fig. 2. Sanskrit consonants with their associated numeric values as specified in the verse.

bhadrambudhisiddhajanmagaṇitaśraddhāmayadbhūpagiḥ

Fig. 3. The verse illustrating an application of the transcription scheme.

dr = 2 (only the last part of the conjoint consonant, r, is considered) mb = 3 (similarly, only the b of mb is considered), etc.

This gives the final value 423,979,853,562,951,413. Since it is known [6, 10], that traditional Indian practice was to write number words in ascending powers of 10, the number represented above, properly, is 314,159,265,358,979,324 which is recognizable to be just the digits of pi to 17 places (except that the last digit is incorrect, it must be 3). Menninger [10] also quotes an example of the Indian name for the lunar cycle being *anantapura,* which in addition to having semantic content itself gives the Katapayadi value 21,600 (using the consonants n-n-t-p-r), which is the number of minutes in the lunar half-month (15 × 24 × 60). (It has been pointed out to me by Dr. Takao Hayashi, Science and Engineering Research Institute, Doshisha University, Japan, in a personal communication, that this does not follow from the most popular Katapayadi coding scheme, since in the conjoint consonant nt. only the t should denote a number.)

The originator of this scheme is not known, as with many other Indian inventions and discoveries, but it is believed that the scheme was probably familiar to the Indian mathematician and astronomer Aryabhata I in the fifth century AD and to Bhaskara I in the seventh century AD [11]. The oldest datable text that employs the scheme is *Grahacaranibandhana* written by Haridatta in 683 AD [12]. The scheme is said to have been used in a wide variety of contexts, including occultisms like numerology. A large number of South Indian chronograms have been composed using this scheme (e.g., reference works such as Epigraphia Indica 3: p. 38, 4: pp. 203-204, 11: pp. 40-41, 34: pp. 205-206). It is also said that Sankara, the Indian philosopher of the seventh century, was named so that the Katapayadi value of his name gives his birthday—215, indicating the fifth day of the first fortnight of the second month in the Indian lunar calendar [13]. Not much else is known about the status or application of this scheme since then. But in the 18th century, we find a novel revival of it in South Indian musicology, which is arguably similar to modern hashing. This is described in the following section.

An Application of the Katapayadi Scheme

In classical South Indian music, the raga is roughly equivalent to the Western chord. These ragas are classified according to a unique scheme. What follows is a brief description of this classification as is pertinent to the subject of this paper. A more comprehensive treatment of Indian musicology, its concepts, and terms can be found in the work by Wade [14].

A raga can be either a *Janaka* (root) raga or a *Janya* raga: the latter is considered to be a descendant of one of the Janaka ragas. The scale of a Janaka raga has seven notes in its ascent and the same seven notes in reverse in its descent. A Janya raga is a modification of its parent Janaka raga through the deletion of one or more notes and/or possibly the reordering of some notes in either or both the ascent and descent of the scale. The seven notes are, respectively, called Sa (*Shadjam*), Ri (*Rishabham*), Ga (*Gandharam*), Ma (*Madhyamam*), Pa (*Panchamam*), Da (*Dhaivatam*), and Ni (*Nishadam*). These are the equivalents of the Western sol-fa syllables Do, Re, Mi, Fa, So, La, and Ti. The notes Sa and Pa (the fifth) are considered fixed and must occur unchanged in all the Janaka ragas. If we consider the octave to consist of the 12 notes C, C#, D, D#, E, F, F#, G, G#, A, A#, and B, since C and G are fixed, Ri and Ga can take any combination of two notes from C#, D, D#, and E. Similarly, Da and Ni can take any combination of two notes from G#, A, A#, and B; and Ma can take any of the two values F or F#. Thus, there can be a total of $2 \times {}^4C_2 \times {}^4C_2 = 72$ possible Janaka ragas. If we arrange these ragas systematically as in Fig. 4, it is possible to derive the notes used by any one of them from its index in the figure. Accordingly, the 72 ragas are arranged as follows: The first 36 ragas use F as the middle note Ma, and the second 36 use F#. In other respects, they are identical. Each half of the grid is further divided into six sections called *chakras,* each of which has six ragas in it. Each of the six *chakras* in each half uses one of the six possible combinations of the notes Ri and Ga, while, within each chakra, the notes Ri and Ga remain constant, but Da and Ni take on each of their six possible combinations.

This classification makes it easy for us to determine the notes of a raga given its serial number in the grid. For example, if we were asked to play the scale of raga number 65, we would know that it uses the note F#, since $65 \div 36 + 1 = 2$. Since $65 \bmod 36 = 29$ and $29 \div 6 + 1 = 5$, we would know that it uses the fifth possible combination of Ri and Ga, which is D and E. Also, since $26 \bmod 6 = 5$, we know it uses the fifth possible combination of Da and Ni, which is A and B. Thus, the scale of Janaka raga number 65 is: C, D, E, F#, G, A, and B.

This means that given the name of a raga, one need only search for its raga number. The notes can be mechanically derived from its number. However, an Indian raga has certain additional musical properties other than the notes it uses. Frequently, a Janya raga that inherits some properties from its Janaka raga is described in terms of the modifications done to its parent that resulted in that particular raga.

These are usually discussed under a description of the Janaka raga and its descendants or, in concise forms, given succinctly alongside its name in a table. To get complete information about a Janaka raga, then, a table search to find its position given its name is presupposed.

F				F*			
Chakra	Ri, Ga	Da & Ni	Raga #	Chakra	Ri, Ga	Da & Ni	Raga #
1	C*, D	G*, A	1	7	C*, D	G*, A	37
		G*, A*	2			G*, A*	38
		G*, B	3			G*, B	39
		A, A*	4			A, A*	40
		A, B	5			A, B	41
		A*, B	6			A*, B	42
2	C*, D*	G*, A	7	8	C*, D*	G*, A	43
		G*, A*	8			G*, A*	44
		G*, B	9			G*, B	45
		A, A*	10			A, A*	46
		A, B	11			A, B	47
		A*, B	12			A*, B	48
3	C*, E	G*, A	13	9	C*, E	G*, A	49
		G*, A*	14			G*, A*	50
		G*, B	15			G*, B	51
		A, A*	16			A, A*	52
		A, B	17			A, B	53
		A*, B	18			A*, B	54
4	D, D*	G*, A	19	10	D, D*	G*, A	55
		G*, A*	20			G*, A*	56
		G*, B	21			G*, B	57
		A, A*	22			A, A*	58
		A, B	23			A, B	59
		A*, B	24			A*, B	60
5	D, E	G*, A	25	11	D, E	G*, A	61
		G*, A*	26			G*, A*	62
		G*, B	27			G*, B	63
		A, A*	28			A, A*	64
		A, B	29			A, B	65
		A*, B	30			A*, B	66
6	D*, E*	G*, A	31	12	D*, E*	G*, A	67
		G*, A*	32			G*, A*	68
		G*, B	33			G*, B	69
		A, A*	34			A, A*	70
		A, B	35			A, B	71
		A*, B	36			A*, B	72

Fig, 4. A systematic arrangement of Janaka ragas.

Things would be even simpler if we could derive the number of a raga directly from its name. This is precisely what was done by the South Indian musicologists. Each raga was named in such a way that a Katapayadi translation of the first two syllables of its name gives us its number in the table. For example, the raga *Mechakalyani* gives us the number 65 (derived from the first two syllables Me and Cha) and Vanaspati gives four. Thus, it is now possible to go directly to the raga's position in its table from its name without having to do a search.

The exact person who coded the names of the ragas seems to be in dispute, but it is fairly certain that such a codification was complete by the end of the 18th century. Aiyyangar [15] states that although Venkatamakhi lays a claim to this arrangement in 1660, it should be credited to his grandson Muddu Venkatamakhi in the early 18th century, who added it as a supplement to the former's work *Chazurdandi Prakasika*.

Discussion

From an observation of the Katapayadi scheme, it seems that there are several important differences between it and modern hashing techniques. Notably, a hashing formula gives a valid bucket number for any given name, but the Katapayadi scheme gives meaningful results for only some names. For example, a true hashing algorithm will never give a number greater than 72 in the above application, whatever the value hashed, but the Katapayadi scheme will.

A hashing algorithm can also take any input and return a number corresponding to its position in a table, whereas in the application of the Katapayadi scheme above, the names of the ragas have been carefully chosen for the purpose. Thus, it seems more probable that the Katapayadi formula was intended as a mnemonic technique to help people remember long numbers. Indeed, the verse from *Sadratnamālā* coding the digits of pi seems to imply just that. In this sense, the scheme is an exact opposite of the modern hashing technique, which aims to derive numbers from names, since it aims to derive names from numbers.

But then its application in South Indian musicology, where there are only 72 admissible root ragas, is clearly directed at liberating the table-lookup operation from the constraints imposed on it by the size of the table. This is the basic aim of a hashing technique. A good hashing algorithm seeks to perform the operations of insertion, deletion, and lookup with constant time complexity. The insert and delete operations are irrelevant to the application outlined above, since the raga names were deliberately coined and already inserted into the table. But once the table had been constructed, lookup took a constant time because of the application of the Katapayadi scheme. The motivation for this must have been similar to a situation that warrants the application of a hashing strategy now—constant time table lookup. The result, too, is the same. Here, it is obvious that it bears a strong similarity to the modern hashing technique. To be sure, the Katapayadi scheme was initially developed as a mnemonic technique, given the oral culture of education in early India. Indeed, Sir Monier Williams remarks [16] that even the grammar of Pāṇini was mainly intended to *"aid the memory of teachers* [rather] *than learners by the briefest possible suggestions."* Nevertheless, it is possible for such a mnemonic technique to gradually evolve into a scheme that bears a strong similarity to our modern hashing technique. It is relatively easy to look at this particular application of the Katapayadi scheme and to come up with a hashing strategy for some modern requirement. But whether the scheme influenced later development of the hashing technique is in doubt. It is not certain whether any Indian scholar with knowledge of this technique was a close associate of any of the proponents of early hashing. And it is not likely that the proponents of hashing knew about the Katapayadi technique. Thus, the most one can say at this stage is that the Katapayadi scheme can be thought of as an early precursor to the modern hash functions, and its application in South Indian musicology bears, in retrospect, an interesting similarity to modern hash tables.

Acknowledgments

The author is grateful to Richard Salomon, Department of Asian languages and literature, University of Washington, and Takao Hayashi, Science and Engineering Research Institute, Doshisha University, Japan, for help in procuring some references. Dr. Hayashi also read the paper and offered several useful comments.

Notes

1. D.G. Severance, "Identifier Search Mechanisms: A Survey and Generalized Model," *Computing Surveys*, vol. 6, no. 3, pp. 175-194, 1974.
2. D.E. Knuth, *The Art of Computer Programming, Vol. 3: Searching and Sorting*. Reading, Mass.: Addison-Wesley, 1973, pp. 541-542.
3. A.I. Dumey, "Indexing for Rapid Random-Access Memory," *Computers and Automation*, vol 5, no 12, pp. 6-9, 1956.
4. R.E. Asher, *The Encyclopaedia of Language and Linguistics*, vol. 6. Oxford, England: Permagon Press, 1994, pp. 2,916-2,918.

5. B. Datta and A.N. Singh, *History of Hindu Mathematics,* Parts 1 and 2, Bombay, India: Asia Publishing House, 1962
6. G. Ifrah. *From One to Zero,* translated by L Bair. New York: Viking Penguin Inc., 1985.
7. J.F. Fleet, "The Katapayadi System of Expressing Numbers," *J. Royal Asiatic Soc.*, BRAS 191 1, pp. 788-794, 1911.
8. C.M. Whish, Transactions of the Literary Society of Madras, Part 1, p. 57, 1827.
9. K.K. Raja, "Astronomy and Mathematics in Kerala: An Account of Its Literature," *Adyar Library Bull.*, vol. 27, pp. 118-167. 1963.
10. K. Menninger, *Number Words and Number Symbols,* translated by P. Broneer, Cambridge, Mass.: MIT Press, 1969.
11. S.N.E. Sen, *A Concise History of Science in India*, New Delhi, India: Indian National Science Academy,1971.
12. K.V. Sarma, "A History of the Kerala School of Indian Astronomy: In Perspective," *Visveshvaranand Indological Series 55,* Visveshvaranand Inst. Publication 580, Visveshvaranand Institute, Hoshiarpur, India, 1972.
13. P. Sambamurthy, *South Indian Music, Book III.* Madras, India: Indian Music Publishing House. 1983, pp. 44-48.
14. B.C. Wade, *Music in India: The Classical Traditions*, Englewood Cliffs, N.J.: Prentice Hall, 1979.
15. R. Aiyyangar, *History of South Indian (Carnatic) Music*, Poona, India: Aryabushan Press, 1972.
16. Sir Monier Williams, *Indian Wisdom,* Banaras, India: Chowkamba Sanskrit Studies, vol. 36, 1969.

The Pāṇini-Backus Form in Syntax of Formal Languages

T.R.N. Rao

Vyaas Houston (1991), in one of his writings, mentions his discovery of the world's oldest living language: Sanskrit, the language of ancient India and Vedic civilization. He states thus:

> "It was perfectly clear to me that I had come upon a perfect language, a language that invokes the spirit, an inexhaustible wellspring of spiritual inspiration. The ancients called it devavani, the language of gods. Where did it come from? — A language infinitely more sophisticated than any of our modern tongues."

The sophistication Houston refers to is about the formalism and structure of the language. For computer scientists, in the theory of formal languages, the word "formal" refers to the fact that all the rules for the language are explicitly stated in terms of what strings of symbols could occur, without any ambiguity and the need for interpretations based on mental skills? Sanskrit not only has a very rich inflectional structure but this fact was recognized early by grammarians and it has contributed to the mystique of the language.

A famous grammar of Sanskrit was compiled by Pāṇini [1], who flourished around 500 B.C., and his work *Aṣṭādhyāyī* has been studied in India for centuries, inspiring many commentaries. The prestige of Pāṇini's grammar is so great that the earlier grammars of the language were lost. Pāṇini's grammar uses a variety of formal techniques including recursion, transformations, and metarules. Here we examine one specific feature of his structure that has been used also in the representation of high-level languages.

The formal structure of computer programming languages was introduced in the 1958-60 period by eminent scientists John Backus (1958), and Peter Naur (1963). They headed UNESCO conferences on International algorithmic language ALGOL 60, a language "suitable for expressing a large class of numerical processes in a form sufficiently concise for direct automatic translation into the language of programmable automatic computers."

What is BNF notation?

BNF is an acronym originally for "Backus Normal Form" that was later changed to Backus-Naur Form. BNF notation can be found in any book on programming languages.

The following, taken from Marcotty and Ledgard (1986), explains the meta-symbols of BNF.

The meta-symbols of BNF are:

::= meaning "is defined as"

| meaning "or"

< > angle brackets used to surround category names.

The angle brackets distinguish syntax rules names (also called nonterminal symbols) from terminal symbols which are written exactly as they are to be represented. A BNF rule defining a nonterminal has the form:

nonterminal ::= sequence_of_altematives consisting of strings of terminals or nonterminals separated by the meta-symbol |

For example, the BNF production for a mini-language is:

<program> ::= program

<declaration_sequence>

begin

<statements_sequence>

end ;

This shows that a mini-language program consists of the keyword "program" followed by the declaration sequence, then the keyword "begin" and the statements sequence, finally the keyword "end" and a semicolon.

Several authors have used slight extensions of BNF for clarification or ease of use which we will not go into.

A point of interest here is a correspondence in ACM Communications from Donald Knuth (1964) arguing on behalf of the acronym BNF to represent Backus-Naur form rather than Backus Normal Form and gives three reasons for that:

1. It gives proper credit to both Backus and Naur for their contributions;
2. It preserves the often used abbreviation "BNF";
3. BNF is not really a "normal form" in any conventional sense or (a special or canonical form) and hence it is just a "form";

Knuth's suggestion prevailed and BNF has been taken to stand for Backus-Naur Form.

Another major point of interest for us is another correspondence in ACM Communications titled "Pāṇini-Backus Form" by P.Z. Ingerman (1967), which we reproduce here verbatim.

> Knuth (1964), in a Letter to the Editor of CACM, makes the point that the metasyntactic notation used in, e.g., the ALGOL 60 report (Naur 1963) should be renamed. In particular, he observes the well-acceded fact that the so-called Backus Normal Form is, indeed, not a normal form in any sense. The purpose of this letter is to observe that Backus was not the first to use the form with which his name has become associated, although he did, indeed, discover it independently.
>
> Dr. Alexander Wilhelmy has called to my attention [2] a work by Pāṇini [3-4]. Pāṇini was a scholar who flourished between 400 B.C. and 200 B.C.; perhaps his most significant work was the compilation of a grammar of Sanskrit. In order to describe the (rather complicated) rules of grammar, he invented a notation which is equivalent in its power to that of Backus, and has many similar properties: given the use to which the notation was put, it is possible to identify structures equivalent to the Backus "|" and to the use of the meta-brackets "<" and ">" enclosing suggestive names. Pāṇini avoided the necessity for the character by writing the meta-result on the right rather than the left [see [5] or Ingerman (1996) for a similar notation].
>
> Since it is traditional in professional circles to give credit where credit is due, and since there is clear evidence that Pāṇini was the earlier independent inventor of the notation, may I suggest the name "Pāṇini-Backus Form" as being a more desirable one? Not only does it give due credit, but it also avoids the misuse of the word "Normal".

Summary

The above makes the powerful plea that Backus-Naur Form (BNF) should be truly called Pāṇini-Backus Form (PBF), as "we must give credit where credit is due." Pāṇinian grammar, which consisted of over 4,000 algebraic rules and metarules have been studied by a number of scholars. Kak (1987), reviews the Pāṇinian approach to natural language processing (NLP) and compares it with the current knowledge representation systems of Artificial Intelligence, and argues that Pāṇinian-style generative rules and metarules could assist in further advances in NLP. Another article by Staal (included in this book) discusses the consistency of the system of rules of Pāṇini, as tested by Fowler's Automaton [6]. These are among the marvelous contributions of ancient India to computing sciences.

References

Backus, John (1959). The syntax and semantics of the proposed international algebraic language of the Zurich ACM-GAMM conference. *Proc. Internat. Conf. Inf. Proc.*, UNESCO, Paris.

Houston, Vyaas (1991). Foreword to "*Gods, Sages and Kings*" by David Frawley, Passage Press, Salt Lake City, Utah.

Ingerman, P.Z. (1966). *A Syntax-Oriented Translator*, Academic Press, New York.

—1967 "Pāṇini-Backus Form Suggested," *Comm. ACM* 10, 3, p. 137.

Kak, S.C. (1987). The Pāṇinian Approach to Natural Language Processing, *International Journal of Approximate Reasoning*; 1:117-130.

Knuth, Donald (1964) Backus normal form vs. Backus Naur form. *Comm. ACM* 7, 12, 735-736.

Marcotty, M. & Ledgard, H. (1986). *The World of Programming Languages*, Springer-Verlag, Berlin, p. 41.

Naur, Peter (Ed.) (1963). Revised report on the algorithmic language ALGOL 60, *Comm. ACM* 6, 1, 1-17.

Vasu, S.C. (1962). The Aṣṭādhyāyī. Motilal Banarsidass, Delhi, India.

Notes

1. Pāṇini. (500 B.C.) The Aṣṭādhyayī. Edited and translated into English by Srisa Chandra Vasu, Delhi. India, 1962.
2. Wilhelmy. A., Private communication dated 5 November 1966.
3. Kavyatirtha, Narayana Rama Acarya (Ed.) Pāṇinimunipranitah astadhyayisutrapathah vartikapathasamalankrtah. Bombay. India, 1954

   [Kavya, N.R.A. (Ed.) Pāṇini—Reading of Rules in Eight Chapters, Embellished by His Pupils]
4. Pāṇini, The Astadhyayi, Edited and translated into English by Srisa Chandra Vasu, Delhi. India. 1962.
5. Irons, E.T., *Maintenance manual for PSYCO—part one*. Institute for Defense Analyses. Princeton, N.J.
6. J.F. Staal, This issue, Chapter 6.

Pāṇini Tested by Fowler's Automaton‡

J. F. Staal

In "How ordered are Pāṇini's rules?" [1] Professor Murray Fowler raises a valid question: can the consistency of the Aṣṭādhyayī (abbreviated as A) be tested by an automaton? Before answering such a question, one should specify what kind of consistency and what kind of automaton one has in mind. I shall begin by considering these preliminaries (1 and 2) and wind up with a brief discussion of the order of Pāṇini's rules (3), showing thereby that Fowler's "cursory examination" (45) is not only inadequate but also misleading.

1.1 Consistency is generally defined as a property of a system of rules. Such a system is called consistent when it is impossible to derive with the help of the rules two results which are, in some sense, contradictory or incompatible. A is consistent in this sense on account of the rule 1.4.2, which says that in case of contradiction between two rules, the following rule prevails. This requires the rules of A to be ordered in a special manner [2].

1.2 For Fowler, consistency requires well-orderedness of linguistic rules, defined as "an arrangement such that the relation of pre-supposition is maintained in a regular progression" (45). More explicitly, a sequence of rules R_1, ..., R_n is called well-ordered if and only if, for no rule R_i there is a later rule R_j presupposed by R_i; or, if and only if:

‡ Reprinted with the permission of the author.

$$(R_i) \neg (ER_j) [(1 \leq i < j \leq n) \wedge (R_i \text{ presupposes } R_j)].$$

Fowler rightly says that the whole of A is not well-ordered in this sense; this follows from the examples he discusses and it does also follow from many others. He is also right where he maintains that attempts at well-ordering the rules (such as Bhattojī Dīkṣita's in the *Siddhānta Kaumudī*) can only be successful if the phrasing of the rules is altered accordingly; in fact it would have to be altered substantially. Fowler concludes that Bhattojī's order, "with the needs of an automaton in mind, seems to be much better than the original." This might be true for a particular kind of automaton (see below) provided the phrasing was altered accordingly; however, this has never been done consistently, not even by Bhattojī Dīkṣita himself, so that, against Fowler, we must agree with Boehtlingk ("*Spätere Grammatiken, die Pāṇini's Sūtra aus der unverrückbaren Ordnung gebracht haben, um alles dem Stoffe nach Zusammengehörige aneinander zu reihen, sind ohne ausführliche Commentare, die stets auf etwas weit Vorangegangenes oder Folgendes Rücksicht nehmen müssen, ganz unverständlich und als Missgriffe zu betrachten*": quoted n.5) and even with Colebrooke ("But the sūtras of Pāṇini, thus detached from their context are wholly unintelligible..." [3]). In fact, the *Siddhānta Kaumudī* is a commentary upon and an introduction to A, not an alternative to it.

It may be noted that the treatment given to Pāṇini's grammar by Bhattojī Dīkṣita is similar to that accorded to Euclid's *Elements* by Petrus Ramus in the XVIth century: Ramus rewrote the *Elements* by ordering the theorems according to topic and omitting the proofs. The logical significance of geometry, i.e., its deductive character, is thereby lost. Bhattojī Dīkṣita and Fowler similarly sacrifice the logical structure of A.

2. Fowler's automaton seems to make sense only if it is interpreted as a finite automaton; in that case, however, it makes no sense in the present context, as we shall see. A finite automaton may be considered to be on a par with a finite state grammar (FSG), which generates a finite state language (FSL). Referring to tests by such an automaton, Fowler states: "Excellent grammars are now being written with this test in mind" (44). In the explanatory footnote he refers to the grammar of C. G. Zull, "A Formal System for generating French Verb Paradigms" (n.2). But a formal system for generating paradigms can at most be part of a grammar, it can never be a grammar in the usual sense: for a grammar is meant to generate sentences.

Now it is well known that the set of English sentences is not a FSL; i.e., it cannot be generated by a FSG [4]. It requires some skill but little originality to show that Sanskrit is not a FSL either. Hence, if A could be shown to be a FSG, it would follow that A would be incapable of describing Sanskrit. Fowler, who indeed suggests that A would probably generate "a highly complex" FSL [5], does not consider adequacy ("conformity with an external object"); but for Pāṇini, as for all grammarians, this is a major concern (formulated in Sanskrit as the requirement of providing rules for all that is loka "common usage"). In other words, Fowler's proof that A is not a FSG is in no way surprising and merely saves A from being seriously inadequate.

This result can also be established directly. Since it has been shown that A contains many context-sensitive rules [6], it follows, not only that A is not a FSG, but that it is not a context-free phrase-structure grammar either. Further, it can be shown that A is also stronger than a context-sensitive phrase-structure grammar, since it contains rules which cannot be written as context-sensitive rules [7]. In short, A contains rules which are strong enough, in principle, to generate Sanskrit sentences; if A were to contain only rules of the kind that can be dealt with by Fowler's automaton, it would be inadequate for describing Sanskrit.

3.1 A slightly more careful perusal of A will show that the order of its rules is in many ways crucial; this has been noted by the Indian commentators, from Patanjali onwards, and by many Western scholars. Fowler is aware of the fact that "the great problem of *anuvṛtti* remains" (47). In fact, the order of the rules of A should be explained in the first place by taking the economy criterion (*lāghava*) and *anuvṛtti* into consideration. Any suggestions for altering the order upset the organization of the grammar in ways which are not always immediately apparent. Discussions of this sort, recently by Shefts [8], for example, have made it quite clear that other features may also influence order. That it is simply a desire to treat certain grammatical topics together which accounts for some features of order, is especially apparent in the case of *anuvṛtti* of *adhikār* as "chapter headings". This has been studied, for example, by Renou [9].

3.2 The earlier quoted meta-rule 1.4.2 [2] introduces another kind of order into A: not connected with the phrasing of rules, but with their actual effect. In these cases altering the order can never be neutralized by reformulation. If the structure of the grammar is to be saved from disruption, there are two alternatives: either the relative order of all pairs of rules to which 1.4.2 is applied must remain the same; or it must be reversed in every case, whilst "following" in 1.4.2 is being replaced by "preceding".

3.3 So far the effect of A on a given input can be described as follows; any rule of A applies to any part of the input, provided the conditions for its application (often formulated as context restrictions) are fulfilled; if, moreover, two rules should provide incompatible results, the latter prevails. But this description holds good (approximately: see 3.4) for (the largest) part of the grammar only: the first seven *adhyāyas* and the first *pāda* of the eighth *adhyāya* (1.1-8.1). For the last three *pādas* of the eighth *adhyāya* (8.2-4) the situation is different: here the rules apply to a given input one after the other in the given order. This part, which is called the *tripādī* and which contains 295 rules (i.e., less than 8% of the total number of rules) begins with the meta-rule and *adhikāra* 8.2.1: *pūrvatrāsiddham* "(From now on every rule is regarded as) not having taken effect with reference to preceding ones." This means that in 8.2-4 no rule applies until earlier rules (either, unordered, in 1.1-8.1 or, ordered, in 8.2-4 itself) have been applied. This rule and its effect have been the subject of a monograph by Buiskool [10].

3.4 However, within 1.1-8.1 also arbitrary applicability of rules is restricted by another application of the principle of *asiddhatva* laid down by meta-rule 50: *asiddham bahirangam antarange* "that which is *bahiranga* is (regarded as) not having taken effect when that which is *antaranga* (is to take effect)." This means that among the rules of A there are many ordered pairs. In each pair, the rule that is applied first is called *antaranga* "inner cause of the operation"; the rule that is applied next is called *bahiranga* "outer cause of the operation."

An example is provided by 6.1.77, iko yan aci which is *antaranga* with respect to 7.3.86 *pugantalaghūpadhasya ca*. The first rule requires, among other things, that i should be replaced by y when followed by a vowel. When applied to *si* + *ū* + *na* this would result in *sy* + *ū* + *na* (1). The second rule requires, among other things, that i and u should undergo *guna* when certain conditions are fulfilled. When applied to *si*

+ *ū* + *na* this would result in *se* + *ū* + *na* (2). Now if (1) is *antaranga* with respect to (2), we obtain first *sy* + *ū* + *na* and next *sy* + *o* + *na*; but if (2) is antaranga with respect to (1), we obtain *se* + *ū* + *na* and there is no scope for (1) to apply. Since, in fact, syona is the correct result, (1) is declared *antaranga* with respect to (2). This principle has been studied by Kielhom [11], Boudon [12], and Renou [13]. The transformational cycle of phonemic rules, whereby innermost brackets are first erased [14], is to some extent reminiscent of this principle.

4. These are some of the features of the types of order underlying Pāṇini's grammar A. These and other features can be fruitfully studied from many points of view. If we distinguish three stages in the study of A as a generative device, it may be held that the first stage, that of analysis, has been dealt with successfully by Indian commentators since Patañjali, and by Western scholars of the last two centuries; however, this task is by no means complete. The second stage, that of formalization, has perhaps just begun to receive attention; it depends on analysis, but is not determined by it. The third stage, that of automation, itself depending on formalization, is not determined by formalization; it may not even be effectively realizable. Despite Fowler's laudable effort, the fact remains that this has been hardly touched upon.

Notes

1. JAOS 85(1965)44-7.
2. See J. F. Staal. "Negation and the law of contradiction: a comparative study", *BSOAS* 25 (1962) 53-6.
3. Preface lo *Laghukaumudī*. ed. J. R. Ballantyne. Benares 1891, ii.

4. See e.g. N. Chomsky, "Three models for the description of language," reprinted in: *Readings in mathematical psychology*. II. ed. Luce, Bush & Galanter, New York & London 1965. 105- 124.

5. 44 n.4, where it is also stated that A "is not very powerfully generative," "because of the absolute necessity of lists to complete it." Is there any grammar that can operate adequately without a lexicon? There is also some confusion about the "evaluation function" mentioned in n.1 with a reference to Lg 39 (1963) 599 n.8, itself a reference to the relevant source.

6. J. F. Staal, "Context-sensitive rules in Pāṇini", *Foundations of Language* 1 (1965) 63-72.

7. Ibid. 68-9.

8. B. Shefts. *Grammatical method in Pāṇini: His treatment of Sanskrit present stems*. New Haven 1961: cf. Lg 39 (1963) 483-8.

9. L. Renou. *Études védiques et Pāninéennes*. I, Paris 1955, 124-6.

10. H. E. Buiskool. *pūrvatrāsiddham: Analytisch onderzoek aangaande het systeem der Tripādi van Pāṇini's Aṣṭādhyayī, Amsterdam 1934; the same, The Tripādi, being an abridged English recast of Pūrvatrāsiddham (An analytical-synthetical inquiry into the system of the last three chapters of Pāṇini's Aṣṭādhyayī*), Leiden 1939.

11. Nāgojībhatta, *Paribhāsenduśekhara*. ed. F. Kielhorn. II, Translation and Notes. Bombay 1874 (ed.[2] K. V. Abhyankar, Poona 1960), 221 sq.

12. P, Boudon. "*Une application du raisonnement par l'absurde dans l'interpretation de Pāṇini*" J A 230 (1938) 65-121: 72-8.

13. L. Renou. *Études védiques et Pāninéennes*. II, Paris 1956. 140 sq.: cf. the same. *La Durghatavrtti de Śaranadeva*. Introduction. Paris 1940, 118-9:

Terminologie grammaticale du Sanskrit. Paris 1957, *s.v. antaranga.*

14. See e.g. N. Chomsky & G. A. Miller, "Introduction to the formal analysis of natural languages", *Handbook of mathematical psychology,* II, ed. Luce, Bush & Galanter. New York & London, 1963, 313-8.

Formal Structures in Indian Logic[§]

J. F. Staal

There is a use of the term "model" in which it can be said that a linguistic expression, in a natural language, is a model for its sense. A translation of a linguistic expression from one language into another may be said to provide another model for the sense of the original. If the sense of a linguistic expression is of a logical nature, the expression can be translated into an expression of formal logic or into a formula. This is not surprising, for logic and mathematics came into being when expressions of natural languages were translated into formal symbolisms, which were more precise and practical and less cumbersome. Subsequently these artificial languages attained full independence and started a development of their own. Originally, however, these symbolisms could only have been constructed along the lines suggested by the possibilities of expression and the scope of expression of the natural languages themselves. That in mathematics and in modern logic such a linguistic origin of the symbolism has often receded into the background does not imply that the origin of certain symbolisms was independent from the structure of natural languages [1].

In view of this background it is not surprising that modern logic could provide the tools for the representation of logical expressions used by the Western logicians from Aristotle onwards. This has been shown by Bochenski, Lukasiewicz

---

[§] Reprinted with permission from Kluwer Academic Publishers.

and many others. It is less evident, on the other hand, that the symbolism of modern logic should be useful in the representation of the only formal logic, regarding which there are good reasons to believe that it developed independently from European logic: namely Indian logic. Nevertheless modern formalisms have been introduced - sometimes hesitatingly - into the study of Indian logic by S. Sen [2], S. Schayer [3], and D.H. H. Ingalls [4]. I.M. Bochenski has now written the first comprehensive history of formal logic which takes Indian material into account [5]. That a modern symbolism can actually be used for the representation of Indian logic at all need not imply that this symbolism is necessarily universal. For Sanskrit, the language in which the Indian logicians expressed themselves even if their mother tongue was different, is an Indo-European language and its structure is largely similar to the structure of for instance Greek or Latin. This holds for its syntax as well as for its analysis of the parts of speech, both structures which are highly relevant for the development of a formal logic.

The origins of Indian logic are invisible, but the disciplines of reasoning developed in the speculations of later Vedic texts as well as in the researches of the Sanskrit grammarians. The famous grammar of Pāṇini (probably IVth century B.C.) reflects a very high level of logical reasoning and can only be considered as the fruit of a long development, most of the traces of which are lost. The oldest logical text which has come down to us is the *Nyāya-sūtra*, which received its present form in the second or third century A.D. From then onwards an extensive logical literature was produced in India by Hindus, Buddhists and Jains. Logical techniques were adopted by some schools of philosophy and criticized and rejected by others. After a long period of logical discussions, in which the Buddhist logicians (e.g. Vasubandhu, Dinnāga, Dharmakīrti) played a large part, a process of re-orientation took place between the Xth and the XIIth century. This culminated in the gigantic work of Gangeśopādhyāya (Gangeśa) (XIIIth century), founder of the "New School" (*navya-nyāya*), when logic became largely free from philosophy, epistemology and cosmology, and the attention was mainly confined to the analysis of inference (*anumāna*). Logic thus became an instrument and a method, and as such it was used in various disciplines. Soon knowledge of the logical terminology and familiarity with the techniques of logical analysis became indispensable for anybody writing on matters philosophical, grammatical, ritual and scientific in general. In the following centuries a new flow of logical literature was produced, mainly in Bengal in North East India. Among the general handbooks then written mention may be made of the *Siddhānta-muktāvalī* or *Kārikāvalī-muktāvalī* of *Viśvanātha Pañcānana* (XVIIth century) upon which the present study is based.

Indian logic has every right to be called formal from Gangeśa, and possibily from the Buddhist logicians onwards. It is formal in as far as it establishes formal rules, the validity of which depends on the structure of the sentence-expressions only. In such expressions variables occur (e.g. "reason", "conclusion") for which constants (e.g. "smoke", "fire") may be substituted. But while the presence and absence of such constants determine the validity of an empirical expression, they do not affect the validity of a logical expression.

The logical expressions are written in a kind of technical Sanskrit, where use is made of certain features of the Sanskrit language which lend themselves to a formalised treatment. Foremost among these features is nominal composition. As it is relevant in the present context to compare Sanskrit in this respect to other Indo-European languages, a recent formulation may be quoted: "The capacity to combine independent words into compound words is inherited by Sanskrit from Indo-European, and similar formations are found in other IE languages. Sanskrit differs from the other IE languages in the enormous development which the system has undergone, which is unparelleled elsewhere." [6]

We have elsewhere studied the relation between these linguistic means of expression and the logical structures [7]. The present paper is based upon a part of the material dealt with in that article, which mainly addresses readers who are familiar with Sanskrit. The present presentation is confined to a representation of Indian expressions by means of symbols and models of modern logic. For the Sanskrit originals the reader may be referred to the other article.

In the following use is made of the terminology of the predicate calculus with equality and in addition of the expression axF(x) denoting the idea "x such that F(x)". We shall make use of the property: $(Ey)(y = axF(x)) \leftrightarrow (Ex)F(x)$. If there are several values of x such that F(x), axF(x) may denote any of these values: e.g. $ax(x^2 = 4)$ may denote either +2 or -2. If (E!x)F(x), there is only one axF(x) which is the same as (ix)F(x).

Two special relations will be introduced in order to represent relationships expressed in the original text: A(x,y) meaning: "x occurs in y", and B(x, y) meaning: "x is the locus of y". In addition we have: $(x)B(x, y) \rightarrow (z)A(z, axB(x, y))$.

We can now proceed to a formulation of the theory of proof. The most direct "means of knowledge" (*pramāṇa*) is perception. Unfortunately, perception is not always available. Sometimes an object which is not perceptible itself can be inferred from a perception. For instance, we may not be able to perceive fire on a distant mountain, but we may perceive smoke; and hence conclude that there is fire because of the smoke.

If a conclusion "s" can be inferred from a reason "h" we shall write V(h,s) (with reference to the initial letters of the Sanskrit terms). A proof or inference consists in showing under which conditions V(h,s) holds. Such a proof can be applied if the validity of these conditions can be established by direct perception. Then V(h,s) is valid, and if "h" is perceived, "s" may be inferred.

It is said in the first instance that V(h,s) is valid if and only if:

1) there is an x such that $x \neq s$;
2) there is a y such that B(y,x), where for x the condition (1) holds;
3) $\neg$ A(h, y), where for y the condition (2) holds.

In other words a first definition of inference can be written as follows:

$$V(h,s) \leftrightarrow \neg A(h, ayB(y, ax(x \neq s))) \qquad \text{(Def. I).}$$

Another definition interchanges the order of the conditions (2) and (3) and can accordingly be written as follows:

$$V(h,s) \leftrightarrow \neg A(h, ay(y \neq axB(x,s))) \qquad \text{(Def. II).}$$

These formulas have been constructed in such a way that there is an isomorphism between the formulas and the Sanskrit expressions in the original. The possibility of this construction is partly due to the use of the a-terminology. Another isomorphism may be established between the formulas and the following figures.

In terms of these schemes V(h,s) is proved whenever it is possible to establish the validity of the three steps which lead from "s" to "h" in the direction indicated by the arrows. The validity in each of these three cases can be established from direct perception.

This approach is not very different from the interpretation of a part of mathematics as a set of inferences of the form: "if the axioms A_1, A_2, ..., A_n are valid, the theorem T_k is valid", etc. In both cases the inference is formulated in all generality, whether the premise is valid or not. In both cases the validity of the inference implies that the conclusion holds whenever the initial conditions or axioms hold.

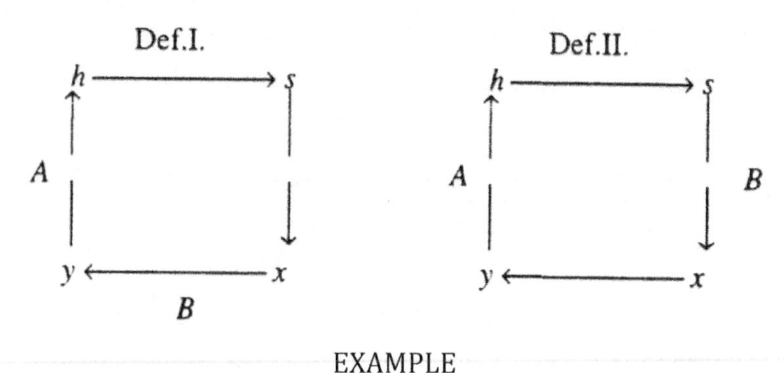

EXAMPLE

V (smoke, fire) is valid:

Def. I.

ax(x≠s): absence of fire.

ayB(y, absence of fire):lake.

┐ A (smoke, lake).

Def. II.

axB(x,s): kitchen.

ay(y≠kitchen):lake.

┐ A (smoke, lake).

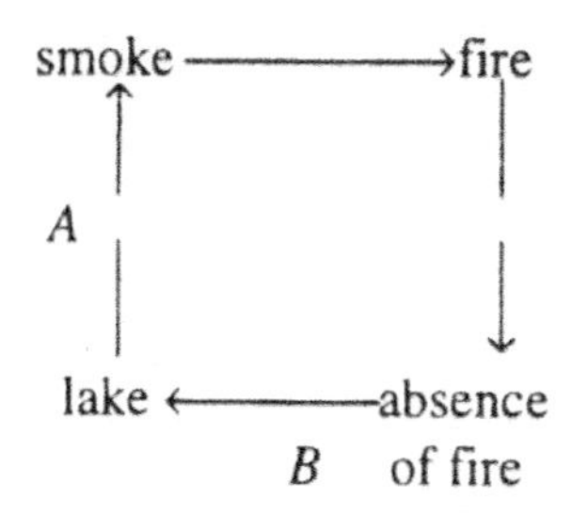

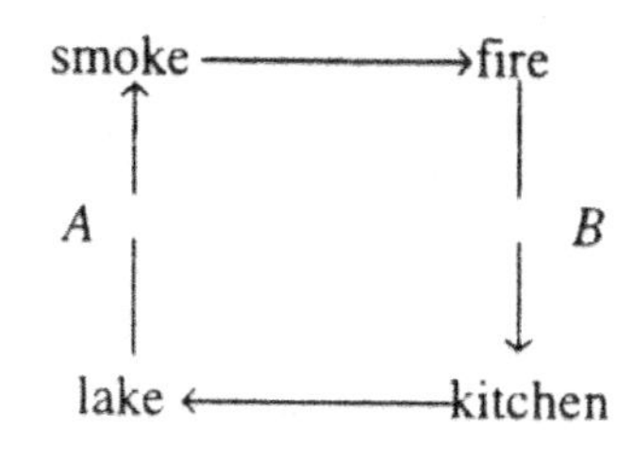

COUNTEREXAMPLE

V (fire, smoke) is invalid:

Def. I.

ax(x≠s): non-smoke.

ayB(y, non-smoke): red-hot iron bar.

A (fire, red-hot iron bar).

Def. II.

axB(x,s): smoky place.

ay(y≠ smoky place): red-hot iron bar.

A (fire, red-hot iron bar).

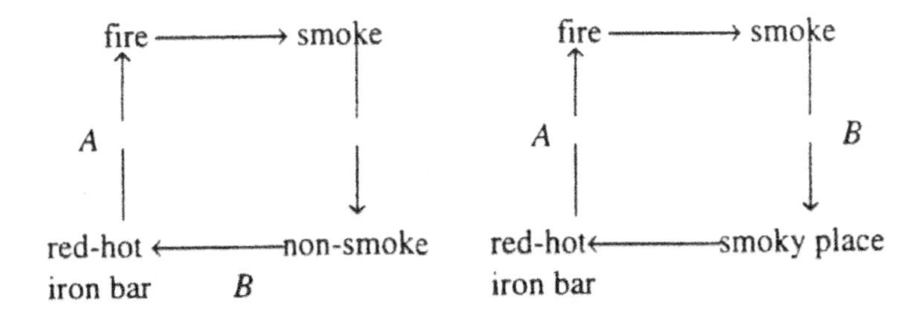

After applying these and other similar definitions to many cases and submitting them to various tests, some definitions are accepted whilst others are rejected. The two definitions mentioned here are rejected for two main reasons, which will be shortly referred to.

a) If $(y)B(y, x)$ then: $(z)A(z,ayB(y,x))$ or: $(z)A(z,ayB(y, ax(x\neq s)))$, which contradicts definition I. Similarly, if $(x)B(x,s)$ then: $\neg$ $(Ey)(y\neq axB(x,s))$, which prevents the application of definition II. Such so-called unnegatable or omnipresent terms, defined by $(x)B(x,s)$, are actually available: for instance "knowable", which may also occur as a conclusion of a proof, for instance in the inference: V (nameable, knowable). Hence the definition should account for the validity of such an inference, although it is unable to do so.

b) There are other cases where the definition does not enable us to prove a conclusion which seems to be intuitively acceptible. As the example produced by the Indian logicians involves abstruse Nyāya categories, a modern example may illustrate the difficulty. Consider again the valid inference V (smoke, fire):

axB(x, fire): kitchen.
ay(y≠kitchen): my mind.
A (smoke, my mind).

Here we have played a kind of trick: while "kitchen" is undoubtedly different from "my mind", "smoke" must occur in "my mind" whenever I think of smoke. Hence the inference seems to be shown to be invalid, though it should be valid. The difficulty lies in the kind of occurrence of "smoke" in "my mind". What is evidently needed is a further precision of the occurrence relation A: the manner in which "smoke" occurs in "my mind" when I think about it is different from the manner in which smoke generally occurs, as examplified by its occurrence (or nonoccurrence) in the kitchen. Now the general place where something occurs whenever it occurs "properly" is called its residence and will be denoted by p. The additional condition, which should hold in order that the definition be valid, is that "h" occurs through A in the same manner in which it occurs in "p". The different kinds of A can now be distinguished by means of bracketed subscripts, such as: $A_{(x)}$, $A_{(y)}$, ... Then the A in definition I (and analogously in definition II), should be specified as follows:

$$azA_{(z)}(h,p) = azA_{(z)}(h,ayB(y,ax(x\neq s)))$$

or:

$$V(h,s) \leftrightarrow \neg A_{(azA_{(z)}(h,p))}(h,ayB(y,ax(x\neq s))).$$

If this is applied to the case of occurrence of "smoke" in "my mind", it is evident that: $azA_{(z)}$ (smoke, my mind) $\neq$ $azA_{(z)}$ (smoke, p).

Hence: $\neg A_{(azA_{(z)}(smoke,p))}(smoke, ay(y\neq axB(x,fire)))$, which establishes the validity of V (smoke, fire).

There are several other insertions to the original definitions, enabling them to meet various tests. One source of difficulties is the lack of quantification, which in the above was partly expressed by the absence of quantifiers and partly by the ambiguity inherent in the expression axF(x). Several insertions consist therefore of gradual quantifications [8]. On the whole many definitions were studied and compared on their respective merits. Some were referred to by special names, such as "the tiger", "the lion" - the authors being nicknamed the Tiger-cub and the Lion-cub. The objection of the unnegatables applies to several definitions and does not seem to have been challenged itself: the final definition, which is accepted after all the others have been convincingly refuted, does not make use of negative expressions.

The study of Navya-nyāya logic is still in its infancy. Of the huge mass of manuscript material only a fragment has been published. Even of the considerable amount of published material only a small part is read. Yet the study of this logic is indispensable for an understanding of the later phases of Indian philosophy.

To Western logicians Indian logic may be interesting because it developed into a formal logic without being influenced by Western logic and starting from an entirely different background. In studying the problem of the universality of logical principles, or the question of the relation between logic and language, it is a great advantage to be able to look beyond the horizon of Western formal logic to the formal logic of India: *"denn sie"*, says Bochenski [9], *und sie allein - bietet dem Historiker eine Möglichkeit von höchster Bedeutung, nämlich die des Vergleichs."*

Note:

The following is from a recent work by Dr. Staal. It will be published in a forthcoming book entitled; *Giant Leaps into the Realm of Knowing.*

> (3) The use of default notions shows that these early scientists were as much concerned with the objects of their scientific description and analysis as with the language of science itself. In ritual, there are many offerings or oblations, many priests, and many implements. It would be counterproductive to mention each time which of these have to be selected. Default applies when no other option is specified. The default oblation is clarified butter; the default priest, the Adhvaryu of the Yajurveda; and the default implement, the ladle called juhū ("tongue"). There are degrees of default: when "tongue" is already used, and

no other implement is specified, the oblation has to be made with the help of another ladle called sruva ("flowing").

The ritual manual of Āpastamba (fifth or fourth century B.C.) uses this default system (one of several) and explains its use by means of four meta-rules in the terse sūtra-style:

24.1.23. When "he makes an oblation" is enjoined, "of clarified butter" should be understood;
24. as agent the Adhvaryu;
25. as implement the juhū
26. when used, with the sruva.

[juhotīti codyamāne sarpirājyam pratīyāt |
adhvaryum kartāram |
juhūm pātram |
vyāprtāyām sruvena ||]

Notes and References

1. Some examples of such dependence are discussed in the present author's "The construction of formal definitions of subject and predicate." to be published in Transactions of the Philological Society.
2. S. Sen. A study on Mathurānātha's *Tattva-cintāmaṇi-rahasya*. Wageningen 1924.
3. S. Schayer. *Über die Methode der Nyāya-Forchung*, Festschrift M. Winternitz. Leipzig 1933, 247-57; and in other publications.
4. D. H. H. Ingalls. Materials for the study of Navya-nyāya logic, Cambridge Mass. 1951. Cf. the present author's review in *Indo-Iranian Journal* 4 (1960), 68-73.
5. I.M. Bochenski, *Formale Logik*, Freiburg/München. 1956, 479-517; "*Die indische Gestalt der Logik*".
6. T. Burrow, *The Sanskrit language*. London 1955, 207-8.

7. "Correlations between language and logic in Indian thought", Bulletin of the School of Oriental and African Studies 23 (1960). 109-122.
8. For instances cf. the present author's "Means of formalisation in Indian and Western logic", Proceedings of the XIIth International Congress of Philosophy (Venice 1958).
9. Op. cit. 486.

Planets in the Vedic Literature**

David Frawley

A deeper examination of Vedic literature reveals a profound tradition of astronomical observation that was previously overlooked, because it is hidden in religious symbolism, not clearly stated in rational terms.

1. Vedic literature reflects a clear tradition of astronomical observation through the 27 or 28 Nakṣatras (constellations of the Moon), along with other astronomical data, including various solstice and equinox positions of great antiquity.
2. Notice of the Nakṣatras, which are often very dim groups of stars, requires notice of the planets, which are brighter even than the brightest stars.
3. The planets are primarily mentioned as a group of five or seven (including the Sun and the Moon) or as 33 or 34 along with 27 or 28 Nakṣatras and the Sun as wives of the Moon.
4. The Vedic ritual was based on union with the Sun, Moon, stars and planets and thereby required an ongoing observation of their positions.
5. The Vedic Gods and seers have astronomical correlations relative to the stars and planets.
6. The Planets can be seen as forms of Soma cups.

** Reprinted with permission from the author and the Indian National Science Academy.

7. The Planets can be seen as forms of Agni, particularly the Planet Mars.
8. Evidence for observation of the Planets appears in Vedic literature through numbers that resemble those of the sidereal and synodic periods of planets, particularly the numbers used in the building of the fire altar, as well as the hymn totals of the different books of the Rg Veda.

Introduction

The Vedic literature, the most ancient literature of India, including the *Brāhmaṇas* and early *Upaniṣads*, contains no listing of the five planets by name. The *Vedāṅga Jyotiṣa*, the earliest Vedic astronomical text, mentions the Sun, Moon and constellations (*Nakṣatra*) but not the planets. The first clear reference to the planets by name is found in the epic, the *Mahābhārata* (Udyoga Parva 143.8-11, Bhīṣma Parva 2.32; 3.11-18, 27- 28), which is generally dated around the second century BC (though much of its material is regarded as several centuries or more older). For this reason some scholars have proposed that the Vedic people were not aware of the planets and knowledge of them came from an outside source, possibly as late as the Greeks after the time of Alexander (300 BC).

There is, however, much evidence to show that the Vedic people did know of the planets, but that existing Vedic literature, being non-astronomical in nature only referred to them indirectly and symbolically, and generally as a group among the other heavenly bodies. The *Vedāṅga Jyotiṣa* being concerned with a calendar depending upon Sun and Moon positions relative to the Nakṣatras did not need to consider the planets and hence does not mention them.

The Vedas contain a system of astronomy dividing the zodiac into 27 or 28 lunar constellations (*Nakṣatras*). The full listing of *Nakṣatras* occurs as early as the *Yajur Veda* (*Taittirīya Saṃhitā* IV.4.10), and *Atharva Veda* (XIX.7), while several *Nakṣatras* and the term *Nakṣatra* itself occur several times in the oldest Vedic text, the *Ṛg Veda*. The *Brāhmaṇas* describe positions of the new, full, or half moon in these *Nakṣatras*, including as beginning the year (for example *Kauṣītaki Brāhmaṇa* IV.4-12; V.l-2).

It should be noted that the *Nakṣatra* system is a highly practical and scientific division of the zodiac, because it provides a different constellation for the Moon to occupy every day. Thereby it allows for precise observation of the Moon's position relative to the stars. Once it is determined what *Nakṣatra* the Moon occupies, the *Nakṣatras* for the remainder of the month will follow in sequence.

The number of *Nakṣatras* being either 27 or 28 is a reflection of the fact that the Moon traverses the zodiac in 27.3 days. To keep the sequence in order a twenty-eighth *Nakṣatra* has to be inserted periodically. This is like the lunar months being 12 or 13 as there are 12.3 lunar months in a year, necessitating the insertion of an occasional intercalary month.

We will not go into the controversial issue of the dating of Vedic texts. The most conservative estimates place them in the pre-Buddhist era from the *Ṛg Veda* to the *Brāhmaṇas* about 1500-700 BC. The most liberal estimates, including those done in light of recent archaeological evidence of the Sarasvatī river in India, pushes the earlier texts before 1900 BC, when the Sarasvatī river which they prominently mention ceased to exist as a perennial stream. This agrees with the astronomy of the texts also. The

Brāhmaṇas place the *Kṛttikās* (Pleiades in Taurus) in the eastern direction (*Śatapatha Brāhmaṇa* II. 1.2.3), the direction of the vernal equinox. The *Atharva Veda* (XIX.7.2) places the solstice (ayana) in Maghā (Leo). Such data reflects a period of around 2500-2000 BC. For information on this subject one can examine my book Gods, Sages and Kings: Vedic Secrets of Ancient Civilization. The point of this particular article is to show that there was a Hindu knowledge of the planets back into the Vedic era.

Nakṣatra Observation Necessitates Notice of the Planets

The *Nakṣatras* often consist of relatively faint stars, third magnitude and dimmer, which are hardly noticeable compared to the brightness of the planets. It is totally illogical to believe that a culture could notice so precisely these dim fixed stars along with the Moon's position within them and not notice the planets which are much brighter than any of the *Nakṣatras*. That the Vedic people knew of the *Nakṣatras* but not the planets would be like stating that a culture knew of the planets but not the Moon. Hence the very existence of the *Nakṣatra* system suggests that the planets were known to the Vedic people.

In fact since a number of the *Nakṣatras* are made up of dim stars it is difficult to note the Moon's position relative to them clearly. The brighter Moon causes several *Nakṣatras* to become almost invisible. In this regard an observation of the planets helps greatly and would be discovered quickly as an additional aid in observation. Jupiter stays in a *Nakṣatra* for over five months, and Saturn for over a year. When one of these bright planets is located in a dim *Nakṣatra*, the *Nakṣatra* can be easily observed through the particular planet located there. The position of the planet could be clearly noted on a moonless night, and then the Moon's conjunction with it would provide an accurate delineation of the Moon's position in it.

The planets follow the same zodiacal band as the Moon and thereby appear as its companions. Judging the Moon's position with the help of the planets on this band is much easier. A number of even brighter *Nakṣatras* (like Svāti or Arcturus) are far removed from the ecliptic and do not provide a precise determination for the Moon's position in the zodiac. Therefore, observation of the *Nakṣatras* would require noting of the planets, particularly the outer planets Mars, Jupiter and Saturn which stay distant from the Sun for long periods of time, to provide clarity in determining *Nakṣatra* positions.

The Term Nakṣatra Originally Included the Planets

There is evidence that the term *Nakṣatra* originally included the planets, along with the Sun and Moon. *Nakṣatra* probably originally meant star or heavenly body, which would naturally include the planets. We should note that all cultures originally included the planets among the stars and discriminated between fixed and moving stars, the latter being the planets. We would expect the same inclusion in the earlier phase of Vedic astronomy.

In the *Mahābhārata* (1.66.16) and *Purāṇas* the *Nakṣatras* are considered to be the daughters of the creator Dakṣa, who were given as wives to the Moon, of which Rohiṇī was the favourite. The Moon as the moving force was considered to be masculine, and the *Nakṣatras* as the places through which he travelled were regarded as feminine.

However, in the *Yajur Veda* (*Taittirīya Saṃhitā* II.3.5.1) the daughters of Prajāpati (another name for the creator Dakṣa) are said to be 33, not 27. They are also given in marriage to the Moon, of which again Rohiṇī is the most favourite. Who were these 33?

It is unlikely that these were 33 constellations, because such a division of the zodiac makes no sense. The division by 27 provides the Moon with a different constellation every day. A division by 33 would cause insurmountable difficulties to calculate, particularly for calendrical purposes, which was the main use of the *Nakṣatras.* If the 33 included extrazodiacal constellations there is no explanation as to how the Moon could unite with them as it would never pass through them. Hence we can rule out the 33 being constellations.

There are 33 Gods in Vedic literature which are said to be the 8 Vasus, 11 Rudras, 12 Ādityas (Suns) and 2 Aśvins. This could not have been the group of 33, as the Vasus and Rudras relate to phenomenon of the earth and atmosphere, not the heavens, and are not considered to be wives of the Moon.

Meanwhile we note that in the *Ṛg Veda* (VII.86.1; X.88.13) the term *Nakṣatra* is used for the Sun. This means that it could have been used for other heavenly bodies like the planets. Elsewhere in the *Ṛg Veda* there are 34 lights of a common nature of which the most important is the Sun.

> Vast is that secret name and all-reaching, through which you generated what has been and what will be. The five beloved ones have entered into its original born beloved light.
>
> He filled the two firmaments and the middle region, the five Gods by the seasons seven by seven. With thirty-four lights of common nature and diverse laws his light spreads in many ways. *Ṛg Veda* X.55.2-3.

The 34 must be the 27 *Nakṣatras*, Sun, Moon and five planets. The five Gods may also be the five planets.

The sacrificial horse, identified with the Sun (*Ṛg Veda* 1.163.2), is divided into 34 parts (*Ṛg Veda* 1.162.18), which are divided according to the seasons (*Ṛg Veda* 1.162.19). As the horse sacrifice (aśvamedha) is one of the most important Vedic rituals, it appears that the planets were included in this symbolism. In fact we note that the *Nakṣatras* are said to be the form (rupa) of the sacrificial horse and the year is said to be his soul (*Yajur Veda, Taittirīya Saṃhitā* VII.5.25; *Bṛhadāraṇyaka Upaniṣad* 1.1). The planets, therefore, must have been among these 34 parts of the horse which is all the *Nakṣatras*, including the Sun.

Therefore, the 33 wives of the Moon are the 27 *Nakṣatras*, the Sun and the five planets and the Moon himself is the thirty-fourth. Affirming this we note that there is an entire hymn in the *Ṛg Veda* (X.85), which also occurs in the *Atharva Veda* (XIV.1), describing the marriage of the Moon God with the Sun Goddess, which apparently occurs at the winter solstice. Just as the Sun and the constellations were regarded as wives of the Moon, so must have been the planets.

The Moon is the fastest moving of the heavenly bodies. In this regard it could be looked upon as the male who activates or fertilizes the other heavenly bodies it comes in contact with, including the Sun and planets which move slower than it does. The *Ṛg Veda* (1.105.10) also speaks of the five bulls that dwell in heaven, which are probably the five planets. As the Moon by moving through the *Nakṣatras* activates them, so must the other planets. To call the planets bulls (ukṣa) suggests this impregnating action. If this action of the planets was known, it must have been watched and calculated.

There are also said to be seven horses of the Sun (*Ṛg Veda* 1.164.2). These seven probably included the Sun, Moon and five planets, as the horse has been identified as having the form of the *Nakṣatras*.

The Vedic Ritual as Gaining the Heavenly Bodies

The heavenly bodies were important to the Vedic religion, in fact central to it. The *Taittirīya Brāhmaṇa* I.V.2 states:

> Those who sacrifice here attain (nakṣate) heaven beyond. This is the nature of the *Nakṣatras* (*Nakṣatrānām Nakṣatratvam*).

The idea is that by the sacrifice one goes to the heavenly bodies and their resident deities. The very term *Nakṣatras* means what is obtained by sacrifice.

A similar verse occurs in the *Ṛg Veda* (X.22.10), which speaks of "the secret of the peoples of the seers who have the power of the *Nakṣatras* (*guhā yadī kavīnām viśām Nakṣatraśavasām*)." Yet more clearly the *Ṛg Veda* states:

> Like a dark horse ornamented with pearls, our fathers (the seers) made the *Nakṣatras.* They placed the darkness in the night and the light within the day. Bṛhaspati broke open the rock and found the rays (cows). *Ṛg Veda* X.68.11.

Not only do the seers gain the stars, the original seers, the Vedic fathers, were regarded as creators of the stars. How could they fail to include the planets among them, the brightest of the stars? Their leader in fact here is Bṛhaspati, whose planetary role as Jupiter would make perfect sense here. Jupiter is the planet that is most regular in its movements, its brightness and its closeness to the ecliptic.

Hence it would quite likely be regarded as a prototype for cosmic law.

Meanwhile, the *Upaniṣads* contain paths that lead to the Sun and the Moon (*Chāndogya* V.10). This again related the goal of Vedic knowledge to the reaching of various heavenly bodies, the foremost of which is the Sun. The *Taittirīya Āraṇyaka* 1.11.49 states:

> The seven seers and Atri, all the Atris and Agastya, dwell with the *Nakṣatras* giving blessings.

The seven seers are identified with the stars of the Big Dipper also called the Bears, *Ṛkṣas*, by the Vedic people. Agastya as the eighth is the star Canopus. However, other stars and the planets have been identified with the *Ṛṣis*. These ideas reflect connections between the stars and karma, such as became the basis for astrology. In this regard the *Mahābhārata* states (Udyoga Parva 29.15), "the *Nakṣatras* beyond shine by karma."

The two main *Ṛṣi* families in the *Ṛg Veda* are the Aṅgirasas, of which Bṛhaspati is the foremost, and the Bhṛgus of which Kavi, Uśanas or Śukra is the most important. Bṛhaspati is the Hindu name of Jupiter and Śukra of Venus in later Hindu astronomy. Bṛhaspati as the priest of the Gods corresponds well with the role traditionally given to Jupiter. Śukra as the priest of the demons as well as the Gods agrees with the role of Venus. In fact one Bhṛgu seer is called Vena (note *Ṛg Veda* X.123), perhaps the ancient Vedic equivalent of the Roman Venus.

While some scholars have argued that the planetary identity of these seers came later, it is difficult to believe that the Vedic people could so faithfully and logically note the *Nakṣatras*, noting where the Moon resided every day, and failed to note Venus and Jupiter which are much brighter than any star! These are the two stars that are most like seers and have ever inspired human beings to greater visions.

In this regard Vedic astronomy employs a 60 year cycle based upon 5 x 12 years, with 12 years being the period of Jupiter's orbit around the Sun. Such a 60 year cycle is found among the Chinese, who also have 28 lunar constellations and call the seven stars of the Big Dipper the seven seers, just as in the Vedic tradition. These traditions are not found in Greek or Babylonian astronomy. Such a *Nakṣatra* related Jupiter calendar would naturally suggest a knowledge of Jupiter along with that system.

In traditional Hindu astrology each planet is related to a particular Vedic seer family, as well as to certain deities. In this regard Indra, the greatest of the Vedic Gods, is associated with the planet Jupiter. This is quite impelling in that Roman Jupiter or *Dyaus Pitar* as the giver of the rains is clearly the Roman equivalent of Vedic Indra.

Yet while the ancients named the planets after their Gods, this does not mean that the Gods and their activities only referred to the planets. We cannot accept all the mythology of the Greco-Roman Gods as planetary in nature, even for deities like Jupiter or Mars who had planetary correspondences. Similarly Vedic Gods like Bṛhaspati or Indra stood for much more than one particular planet. The point is that we cannot exclude the planets from their symbolism.

Planetary Mythology

The Hindu names of the planets and their mythology is uniquely Hindu, which is another reason why one cannot easily attribute knowledge of them to a foreign influence.

Hindu mythology of the planets is given in terms of Vedic and Hindu Gods like Viṣṇu, who is the deity of Mercury, and Śiva, whose son, Skanda, relates to the planet Mars, Bṛhaspati and Jupiter, Śukra and Venus, Yama and Saturn.

Most interestingly the two main families of Vedic seers, are the Aṅgirasas and the Bhṛgus, with Jupiter (Bṛhaspati) and Venus (Śukra) who are their main leaders. These two groups often struggled. The Bhṛgus as the gurus of the Daityas or demons, and the Aṅgirasas as the gurus of the Gods become involved in the famous war between the Devas and Asuras (demons). This began when Bṛhaspati's (Jupiter's) wife Tārā (meaning the stars), was abducted by Soma (the Moon). This led to a war in heaven. Śukra (Venus) aligned himself with the Moon and the demons. Rudra (apparently Mars) aligned himself with Jupiter and the Gods. Tārā gave birth to Budha (Mercury) who is accepted as a son by both Jupiter and the Moon, though he was actually the son of the Moon.

This story contains an astronomical riddle. Jupiter is the brightest star in the night sky, and as such rules over the other stars. When the Moon appears however, it steals the light of the stars or metaphorically speaking takes away Jupiter's wife. Venus, which can never get far from the Sun, appears only in the morning or evening sky, not in the dark of night when Jupiter reigns supreme. Hence Venus is allied with the Moon. Mars similarly is allied with Jupiter as a night star. Mercury appears like a night star, lacking the brilliance of Venus, but is found only close to the Sun in the twilight hours, thus allying itself with Venus and the Moon.

This story is furthermore related to the original Vedic kings and ancestor figures. Vedic lineages start with Manu. the Vedic original man, who is said to be the son of the Sun.

He has a daughter named Ilā (which also means speech). She marries Budha (Mercury, the planet of speech), the son of the Moon (Soma), which was during the time of the war between the Gods and Demons. This starts the lunar dynasty of kings which was the main dynasty that ruled ancient India.

We should also note that Manu has a twin brother named Yama, who became the God of death, and was also the son of the Sun. In Hindu mythology Saturn is also a son of the Sun and the God of death.

This battle between the Moon and Jupiter suggests that the Vedic people not only noticed the *Nakṣatra* of the Moon but also that of Jupiter. Jupiter stays in a *Nakṣatra* around 160 days, meaning that it covers two *Nakṣatras* in the *Nakṣatra* year of 324 (12 x 27) days. The Jupiter calendar as mentioned in later astronomical texts was an imitation of the Moon (Sūrya Siddhānta XIV. 17).

The Planets as Graha or Soma Cups

The *Atharva Veda* contains clear references to the planets and the nodes of the Moon in a hymn that relates to various astronomical and meteorological phenomena. For the planets it uses the term *graha*, which is the classical Sanskrit term for them.

> May the earthly and atmospheric powers be peaceful to us. May the planets that move in Heaven (*divicarā grahāḥ*) give us peace. May the planets (*grahāḥ*) and the Moon give us peace. May the Sun and Rāhū give us peace. *Atharva Veda* XIX.97.10.

This hymn not only mentions the planets but also Rāhū or the north node of the Moon, which suggests a knowledge of eclipses and possibly the ability to predict them. Another name for Rāhū, Svarbhānu appears in *Ṛg Veda*

(V.40). Yet another hymn from the *Ṛg Veda* (X.72.9), while speaking of the seven sons of Aditi or Ādityas, whom I would identify with the Sun and Moon and five planets, adds an eighth called Mārtaṇḍa or the mortal egg, which is responsible for birth and death. This eighth sun which is imperfectly born or mortal, I would also identify with Rāhū. The eclipses of the Sun reflects the births and deaths of creatures, as each time the Sun is eclipsed it dies and is reborn.

The term for planet, *graha*, is very interesting, because it is a ritualistic Vedic term for the cups of Soma that can be offered to the different Gods. The Soma cup is well known to be the Moon which is filled during the waxing half and emptied during the waning half.

> The wise sages with their words fashion the one being, the eagle, in various ways. Sustaining the meters in the rituals, they measure twelvefold the cups of Soma (*grahāntsomasya mimate dvādaśa*). *Ṛg Veda* X. 114.5.

The twelve *grahas* are obviously the twelve moons of the year. The planets, like the Moon, also have their motions whereby they wax and wane. This is most true of the planets which are inferior to the earth's orbit, namely Venus and Mercury. Venus most noticeably fills with light as it moves from the Sun and loses that light as it falls back into the Sun and disappears. Yet Mars also goes through significant fluctuations of brightness during its synodic period. Undoubtedly, the term *graha* for planet arose from this observation of the fluctuations in planetary light like the Moon. The term *graha*, thereby, suggests an observation of the waxing and waning of the brightness of the planets through their synodic periods.

The term *graha* for planet indicates that the planets may have been an integral part of rituals wherein different cups or *grahas* were offered to the God (who himself is Heaven or the Sun). The planets may have been considered to be different types of Soma cups.

Two Soma cups are particularly interesting. One is Śukra said to relate to the Sun and Manthin related to the Moon (Śatapatha Brāhmaṇa IV.2.1.2). Śukra as a name for Venus may be meant here, as the brightest star it could be related to the Sun. Manthin could be Mercury who is the son of the Moon in Vedic astrology.

The *Ṛg Veda* (IX.114.3) speaks of seven suns (Ādityas) relative to the seven directions, which may be the Sun, Moon and five planets. They are related to the seasons, which in India are six with the seventh being the Sun as the year (samvatsara). In classical Vedic astrology the six seasons of spring, summer, rains, autumn, the cold and the frosty seasons are ruled by Venus, Mars, Moon, Mercury, Jupiter and Saturn. This may reflect an earlier Vedic view. The six seasonal Soma cups (*ṛtu graha*) may have had planetary correspondences.

Planets and Agni

The planets would also be likely to be regarded as forms of Agni or the Vedic sacred fire. The reason is that when fire rituals were done at night, the stars would be imagined to be like sparks from the fire and Agni rules all forms of light.

In Hindu mythology since the *Mahābhārata* (Vana Parva 223-233) the deity ruling Mars, Skanda, the son of Śiva, is said to take birth through Agni. Skanda is born in the same *Kṛttikā Nakṣatra* ruled by Agni (which rulership is first mentioned in the *Atharva Veda* XIX.7 and *Yajur Veda*

Taittirīya Saṃhitā IV.4.10). Skanda has six mothers as the (*Kṛttikā*) Pleiades and the seventh which is Umā (Pārvatī). Agni in the *Ṛg Veda* is also said to have been conceived by seven mothers or seven voices (*Ṛg Veda* III. 1.6).

Agni has several forms. In his universal form he is the Sun. Vaiśvānara Agni. Yet he also has the form of a child (Kumāra), which is related not only to Skanda but to Rudra. This child form of Agni appears to be related to the night and to the Earth. In Hindu thought, Mars is considered to be the son of the Earth, and Agni is enkindled in the Earth altar (Vedī). Earth corresponds to the night as Heaven is with the day. Hence Agni the child may be the same as Mars-Skanda, the warrior-child.

Those practicing fire rituals at night and noting the Nakṣatras would be compelled to identify Agni with Mars. Mars is the red and fiery planet. It also undergoes significant changes in its brightness through its synodic period.

Mars in Hindu thought is also associated with agriculture as Kṣetrapati or the Lord of the field (*Ṛg Veda* IV.57.2, which verse is used for the worship of Mars in later rituals). Perhaps Mars moving through the sky was thought to imitate the ploughing of the Earth. Vedic agriculture began with the burning of the land by fire. Hence Agni also relates to agriculture. Agni in his child form emerges from the field, preparing his weapons (*Ṛg Veda* V.2.2-3).

Planetary Periods

There are two types of planetary periods, synodic and sidereal. The synodic period measuring the period between the two brightest appearances of the planet was probably the most important of the two. This fluctuation of brightness is most in evidence relative to Mercury (116 days) and Venus

(584 days), the inferior planets. Yet Mars as a superior planet has a noticeable synodic period (780 days). The synodic periods of Jupiter and Saturn are much less noticeable in their fluctuations and not much longer than a year (399 days and 378 days). As Mercury is always close to the Sun and difficult to observe, one would expect that the synodic periods of Venus and Mars would have been more likely to have been noted.

The sidereal periods of Mercury is (88 days) and Venus (225 days). Of these periods those of the superior planets, particularly Jupiter and Saturn would be more evident measures of time because of their greater length (4333 days and 10,760 days, which approximate 4320 and 10,800). The period of Mars is 687 days. The number 432 (*Ṛg Veda* IV.58.1) and its various multiples is common in Vedic lore, so is the number 108 and 10,800 (*Śatapatha Brāhmaṇa* X.4.2.25). The importance of these numbers may reflect at least in part an approximation of the periods of these planets (though this is not explicitly stated anywhere).

The Vedic fire altar (*Śatapatha Brāhmaṇa* X.4.3.13) is enclosed by three Layers of bricks [2] for the three worlds of Earth, Atmosphere and Heaven, consisting of 21, 78 and 261 for a total of 360. 78, the atmospheric number, is 1/10 of the synodic period of Mars (780 days). 261, the heavenly number (which would include the stars), is 1/3 of the synodic period of Mars plus one.

That numbers for Mars would appear in the Vedic fire altar makes sense owing the later Hindu identification of Mars and Agni, the Vedic fire. The synodic period would be more important as it measures the fluctuations of Mars between its dimmest and brightest appearances, mimicking the enkindling and blazing up of the fire altar.

Such correspondences with Mars, however, need not exclude other correspondences to various calendrical or astronomical considerations that can also be found in these numbers. The Vedic sages would have created as many sides and comprehensive a symbology as possible in the Vedic attempt to recreate the entire universe in the ritual.

The Ṛgvedic Astronomical Code of Subhash Kak

Subhash Kak has shown that the numbers of the hymn totals in the different books of the *Ṛg Veda* contains much astronomical information including the *Nakṣatra* year (324 days), the lunar year (354 days), the distance between the Sun and the earth (108 solar diameters) and both the synodic and sidereal periods of the planets [3]. Such numbers were encrypted in various combinations that are beyond any mere chance occurrence. The information in this article gives additional information to support that the Vedic people observed the planets.

Conclusions

In the early Vedic period the planets were included among the *Nakṣatras* or stars as the 34 lights or 33 wives of the Moon. About the time of the Yajur Veda the term *Nakṣatra* became more limited in meaning to the fixed star systems along the zodiac 27 or 28 in number. At this time the planets became differentiated as Soma cups (*graha*), and a more defined mythology of the planets gradually emerged including Vedic deities and Vedic seers, yet with probable antecedents going back to the *Ṛg Veda*.

Astronomy in the Vedic period to the time of the *Brāhmaṇas* included noting the position of the Moon (and Sun) in the 28 *Nakṣatras* noting solstice points, as the Vedic ritual year began with the winter solstice (note *Kauṣītaki Brāhmaṇa* XIX 3).

It also involved a calculation of the phases of the Moon and the lunar days or Tithis (a 30 fold division of the lunar month of 29.5 days). In addition, it must have noted the movements of the planets, particularly the Moon's conjunction with them. Such combinations (lunar yogas) are well explained in classical Vedic astrology which has no real counterpart among the Greeks.

The Vedic ritualists saw union with the heavenly bodies as the goal of their practice. This could include merging into the Sun, the Moon, the *Nakṣatras* or other stars (like the stars of the Big Dipper or Canopus). It must have, therefore, included the planets as well. The Vedic seer families of the Aṅgirasas and Bhṛgus associated themselves with the planets Jupiter and Venus as these were the two brightest planets. There may have been longer Vedic calendars based upon these planets, like the 60 year cycle of Jupiter. The Vedic kings traced their descent from the Sun and Moon apparently with symbolic connections with Mercury, and with Jupiter and Venus as relating to their priestly guides, the Aṅgirasas and Bhṛgus. Hence there are strong astronomical considerations throughout the Vedas suggesting an early and independent tradition of astronomical observation, including the planets. This matter requires further exploration, which necessitates giving up the idea that there is no real astronomy or mathematics in the Vedas, which now appears as no more than a prejudice of Eurocentric thinking.

Vedic Texts

Atharva Veda. Ajmer, India: Śrīmatī Paropakāriṇī Sabhā, 1974.

Mahābhārata. Gorakhpur, India: Gita Press, 1980.

Ṛg Veda, Ed. S.D. Sātvalekar. Paradi, India: Svadhyaya Mandala, 1976.

Śāṅkhāyana Brāhmaṇa (*Kauṣītaki Brāhmaṇa*). Varanasi, India: Ratna Publications 1987.

Śatapatha Brāhmaṇa. Delhi, India: Nag Publishers 1990.

Sūrya Siddhānta. Burgess and Whitney trans. San Diego: Wizards Bookshelf 1978.

Taittirīya Āraṇyaka. Delhi, India: Motilal Banarsidass, 1984.

Taittirīya Saṃhitā, Ed. S.D. Satvalekar. Bahalgarh, India: Yudhisthira Mimamsaka, 1988.

Vedāṅga Jyotiṣa of Lāgadha, T.S. Kuppanna Sastry. New Delhi, India, Indian National Science Academy, 1985.

References

1. Frawley, David. *Gods. Sages and Kings: Vedic Secrets of Ancient Civilization*. Salt Lake City: Passage Press, 1991 and Delhi. India: Motilal Banarsidass 1993: Rajaram. Navaratna and David Frawley. *Vedic Aryans and the Origins of Civilization*. St Hyacinthe, Canada: World Hentage Press 1994.
2. Kak. Subhash. "Astronomy in the Śatapatha Brāhmaṇa. *Indian J. of History of Science*, 28, 15-34. 1993; Kak, Subhash. "The structure of the Ṛgveda", *Indian J. of History of Science*, 28. 71-79, 1993; Kak, Subhash. *Current Science*, Vol. 66, No. 4, 323-326, 1994.
3. Kak, Subhash. *The Astronomical Code of the Ṛgveda*. New Delhi: Aditya Prakashan, 1994.

The Speed of Light and Puranic Cosmology

Subhash Kak

Indian texts consider light to be like a wind. Was any thought given to its speed? Given the nature of the analogy, one would expect that this speed was considered finite. The Purāṇas speak of the moving *jyotiścakra*, "the circle of light." This analogy or that of the swift arrow let loose from the bow in these accounts leaves ambiguous whether the circle of light is the Sun or its speeding rays.

We get a specific number that could refer to the speed of light in a medieval text by Sāyaṇa (c. 1315-1387), prime minister in the court of Emperors Bukka I and his successors of the Vijayanagar Empire and Vedic scholar. In his commentary on the fourth verse of the hymn 1.50 of the *Ṛgveda* on the Sun, he says [1]:

> *tathā ca smaryate yojanānām sahasre dve dve śate dve ca yojane ekena nimiṣārdhena kramamāna*
>
> Thus it is remembered: [O Sun] you who traverse 2,202 yojanas in half a nimeṣa.

The same statement occurs in the commentary on the Taittirīya Brāhmaṇa by Bhaṭṭa Bhāskara (10th century?), where it is said to be an old Purāṇic tradition.

The figure could refer to the actual motion of the Sun but, as we will see shortly, that is impossible. Is it an old tradition related to the speed of [sun]light that

Sāyaṇa appears to suggest? We would like to know if that supposition is true by examining parallels in the Purāṇic literature.

The units of yojana and nimeṣa are well known. The usual meaning of yojana is about 9 miles as in the Arthaśāstra where it is defined as being equal to 8,000 dhanu or "bow," where each dhanu is taken to be about 6 feet. Āryabhaṭa, Brahmagupta and other astronomers used smaller yojanas but such exceptional usage was confined to the astronomers; we will show that the Purāṇas also use a non-standard measure of yojana. As a scholar of the Vedas and a non-astronomer, Sāyaṇa would be expected to use the "standard" Arthaśāstra units.

The measures of time are thus defined in the Purāṇas:

15 nimeṣa = 1 kāṣṭhā
30 kāṣṭhā = 1 kalā
30 kalā = 1 muhūrta
30 muhūrta = 1 day-and-night

A nimeṣa is therefore equal to 16/75 seconds.

De and Vartak have in recent books [2] argued that this statement refers to the speed of light. Converted into modern units, it does come very close to the correct figure of 186,000 miles per second!

Such an early knowledge of this number doesn't sound credible because the speed of light was determined only in 1675 by Roemer who looked at the difference in the times that light from Io, one of the moons of Jupiter, takes to reach Earth based on whether it is on the near side of Jupiter or the far side. Until then light was taken to travel with infinite velocity. There is no record of any optical experiments that could have been performed in India before the modern period to measure the speed of light.

Maybe Sāyaṇa's figure refers to the speed of the Sun in its supposed orbit around the Earth. But that places the orbit of the Sun at a distance of over 2,550 million miles. The correct value is only 93 million miles and until the time of Roemer the distance to the Sun used to be taken to be less than 4 million miles. This interpretation takes us nowhere. The Indian astronomical texts place the Sun only about half a million yojanas from the Earth.

What about the possibility of fraud? Sāyaṇa's statement was printed in 1890 in the famous edition of Ṛgveda edited by Max Müller, the German Sanskritist. He claimed to have used several three or four hundred year old manuscripts of Sāyaṇa's commentary, written much before the time of Roemer.

Is it possible that Müller was duped by an Indian correspondent who slipped in the line about the speed? Unlikely, because Sāyaṇa's commentary is so well known that an interpolation would have been long discovered. And soon after Müller's *"Rigveda"* was published, someone would have claimed that it contained this particular "secret" knowledge. Besides, a copy of Sāyaṇa's commentary, dated 1395, is preserved in the Central Library, Vadodara [3].

One can dismiss Sāyaṇa's number as a meaningless coincidence. But that would be a mistake if there exists a framework of ideas—an old physics—in which this number makes sense. We explore the prehistory of this number by considering early textual references. We will show that these references in the Purāṇas and other texts indicate that Sāyaṇa's speed is connected, numerically, to very ancient ideas. This helps us understand the framework of ideas regarding the universe that led to this figure.

Physical Ideas in the Indian Literature

The Vedas take the universe to be infinite in size. The universe was visualized in the image of the cosmic egg, Brahmāṇḍa. Beyond our own universe lie other universes.

The *Pañcaviṃśa Brāhmaṇa* 16.8.6 states that the heavens are 1000 earth diameters away from the Earth. The Sun was taken to be halfway to the heavens, so this suggests a distance to the Sun to be about 500 earth diameters from the Earth, which is about 0.4375 million yojanas.

Yajurveda, in the mystic hymn 17, dealing with the nature of the universe, counts numbers in powers of ten up to 10^{12}. It has been suggested that this is an estimate of the size of the universe in yojanas.

The philosophical schools of *Sāṃkhya* and *Vaiśeṣika* tell us about the old ideas on light [4]. According to *Sāṃkhya*, light is one of the five fundamental "subtle" elements (tanmātrā) out of which emerge the gross elements. The atomicity of these elements is not specifically mentioned and it appears that they were actually taken to be continuous.

On the other hand, *Vaiśeṣika* is an atomic theory of the physical world on the nonatomic ground of ether, space and time. The basic atoms are those of earth (pṛthivī), water (*āpas*), fire (*tejas*), and air (*vāyu*), that should not be confused with the ordinary meaning of these terms. These atoms are taken to form binary molecules that combine further to form larger molecules [5]. Motion is defined in terms of the movement of the physical atoms and it appears that it is taken to be non-instantaneous.

Light rays are taken to be a stream of high velocity of tejas atoms. The particles of light can exhibit different characteristics depending on the speed and the arrangements of the tejas atoms.

Although there existed several traditions of astronomy in India [6], only the mathematical astronomy of the Siddhāntas has been properly examined. Some of the information of the non-Siddhāntic astronomical systems is preserved in the Purāṇas.

The Purāṇic astronomy is cryptic, and since the Purāṇas are encyclopaedic texts, with several layers of writing, presumably by different authors, there are inconsistencies in the material. Sometimes, speculative and the empirical ideas are so intertwined that without care the material can appear meaningless. The Purāṇic geography is quite fanciful and this finds parallels in its astronomy as well.

We can begin the process of understanding Purāṇic astronomy by considering its main features, such as the size of the solar system and the motion of the Sun. But before we do so, we will speak briefy of the notions in the Siddhāntas.

Size of the Universe in the Āryabhaṭiya

Āryabhaṭa in his Āryabhaṭiya (AA) deals with the question of the size of the universe. He defines a yojana to be 8,000 nr, where a nr is the height of a man; this makes his yojana (y_a) approximately 7.5 miles [7]. Or y_s = 6/5 y_a, where y_s is the standard Arthaśāstra yojana. AA 1.6 states that the orbit of the Sun is 2,887,666.8 yojanas and that of the sky is 12,474,720,576,000 yojanas.

Commenting on this, Bhāskara I (c. 629) says:

> *yāvantamākaśapradeśam ravermayūkhāh samantāt dyotayanti tāvān pradeśah khagolasya paridhih khakaksyā. anyatha hyaparimitatvāt ākāśasya parimānākhyānam nopapadyate.*
>
> That much of the sky as the Sun's rays illumine on all sides is called the orbit of the sky. Otherwise, the sky is beyond limit; it is impossible to state its measure [8].

This implies that while the universe is infinite, the solar system extends as far as the rays of the Sun can reach.

There is no mention by Āryabhaṭa of a speed of light. But the range of light particles is taken to be finite, so it must have been assumed that the particles in the "observational universe" do not penetrate to the regions beyond the "orbit of the sky." This must have been seen in the analogy of the gravitational pull of the matter just as other particles fall back on Earth after reaching a certain height.

The orbit of the sky is 4.32×10^6 greater than the orbit of the Sun. It is clear that this enlargement was inspired by cosmological ideas.

The diameters of the Earth, the Sun, and the Moon are taken to be 1,050, 4,410 and 315 yojanas, respectively. Furthermore, AA 1.6 implies the distance to the Sun, R_s, to be 459,585 yojanas, and that to the Moon,

R_m, as 34,377 yojanas. These distances are in the correct proportion related to their assumed sizes given that the distances are approximately 108 times the corresponding diameters [9].

Converted to the standard Arthaśāstra units, the diameters of the Earth and the Sun are about 875 and 3,675 yojanas, and the distance to the Sun is around 0.383 million yojanas.

Āryabhaṭa considers the orbits, with respect to the Earth, in the correct order Moon, Mercury, Venus, Sun, Mars, Jupiter, and Saturn, based on their periods.

Purāṇic Cosmology

The Purāṇas provide material which is believed to be closer to the knowledge of the Vedic times [10]. Here we specifically consider Vāyu Purāṇa (VaP), Viṣṇu Purāṇa (ViP), and Matsya Purāṇa (MP). VaP and ViP are generally believed to be amongst the earliest Purāṇas and at least 1,500 years old. Their astronomy is prior to the Siddhāntic astronomy of Āryabhaṭa and his successors.

The Purāṇas instruct through myths and this mythmaking can be seen in their approach to astronomy also. For example, they speak of seven underground worlds below the orbital plane of the planets and of seven "continents" encircling the Earth. One has to take care to separate this imagery, that parallels the conception of the seven centres of the human's psychosomatic body, from the underlying cosmology of the Purāṇas that is their primary concern in their *jyotiṣa* chapters.

It should be noted that the idea of seven regions of the universe is present in the *Ṛgveda* 1.22.16-21 where the Sun's stride is described as *saptadhāman*, or taking place in seven regions.

The different Purāṇas appear to reproduce the same cosmological material. There are some minor differences in figures that may be a result of wrong copying by scribes who did not understand the material. In this paper, we mainly follow ViP.

ViP 2.8 describes the Sun to be 9,000 yojanas in length and to be connected by an axle that is 15.7 x 106 yojanas long to the *Mānasa* mountain and another axle 45,500 yojanas long connected to the pole star. The distance of 15.7 million yojanas between the Earth and the Sun is much greater than the distance of 0.38 or 0.4375 million yojanas that we find in the Siddhāntas and other early books. This greater distance is stated without a corresponding change in the diameter of the Sun. It is interesting that this distance is less than one and a half times the correct value; the value of the Siddhāntas is one-thirtieth the correct value.

Elsewhere, in VaP 50, it is stated that the Sun covers 3.15 million yojanas in a *muhūrta*. This means that the distance covered in a day are 94.5 million yojanas. MP 124 gives the same figure. This is in agreement with the view that the Sun is 15.7 million yojanas away from the Earth. The specific speed given here, translates to 116.67 yojanas per half-nimeṣa.

The size of the universe is described in two different ways, through the "island-continents" and through heavenly bodies.

The geography of the Purāṇas describes a central continent, Jambu, surrounded by alternating bands of ocean and land. The seven island- continents of Jambu, Plakṣa, Śalmala, Kuśa, Krauñca, Śāka, and Puṣkara are encompassed, successively, by seven oceans; and each ocean and continent is, respectively, of twice the extent of that which precedes it. The universe is seen as a sphere of size 500 million yojanas.

It is important to realize that the continents are imaginary regions and they should not be confused with the continents on the Earth. Only certain part of the innermost planet, Jambu, that deal with India have parallels with real geography.

The inner continent is taken to be 16,000 yojanas as the base of the world axis. In opposition to the interpretation by earlier commentators, who took the increase in dimension by a factor of two only across the seven "continents," we take it to apply to the "oceans" as well. At the end of the seven island-continents is a region that is twice the preceding region. Further on, is the Lokāloka Mountain, 10,000 yojanas in breadth, that marks the end of our universe.

Assume that the size of the Jambu is J yojana, then the size of the universe is:

$$U = J\,(1+2+2^2+2^3+2^4+2^5+2^6+2^7+2^8+2^9+2^{10}+2^{11}+2^{12}+2^{13}+2^{14}) + 20{,}000 \qquad (1)$$

Or,

$$U = 32{,}767J + 20{,}000 \text{ yojanas} \qquad (2)$$

If U is 500 million miles, then J should be about 15,260 yojanas. The round figure of 16,000 is mentioned as the width of the base of the Meru, the world axis, at the surface of the Earth. This appears to support our interpretation.

Note that the whole description of the Purāṇic cosmology had been thought to be inconsistent because an erroneous interpretation of the increase in the sizes of the "continents" had been used.

When considered in juxtaposition with the preceding numbers, the geography of concentric continents is a representation of the plane of the Earth's rotation, with each new continent as the orbit of the next "planet" [11].

The planetary model in the Purāṇas is different from that in the Siddhantas. Here the Moon as well as the planets are in orbits higher than the Sun. Originally, this supposition for the Moon may have represented the fact that it goes higher than the Sun in its orbit. Given that the Moon's inclination is 5° to the ecliptic, its declination can be 28.5° compared to the Sun's maximum declination of ±23.5°. This "higher" position must have been, at some stage, represented literally by a higher orbit. To make sense with the observational reality, it became necessary that the Moon is taken to be twice as large as the Sun.

The distances of the planetary orbits beyond the Sun are as follows:

Table 1: From Earth to Pole-star

Interval I	yojanas
Earth to Sun	15,700,000
Sun to Moon	100,000
Moon to Asterisms	100,000
Asterisms to Mercury	200,000
Mercury to Venus	200,000
Venus to Mars	200,000
Mars to Jupiter	200,000
Jupiter to Saturn	200,000
Saturn to Ursa Major	100,000
Ursa Major to Pole-star	100,000
Sub-total	17,100,000

Further spheres are postulated beyond the pole-star. These are the Maharloka, the Janaloka, the Tapoloka, and the Satyaloka. Their distances are as follows:

Table 2: From Pole-star to Satyaloka

Interval II	yojanas
Pole-star to Maharloka	10,000,000
Maharloka to Janaloka	20,000,000
Janaloka to Tapoloka	40,000,000
Tapoloka to Satyaloka	120,000,000
Grand Total	207,100,000

Since the last Figure is the distance from the Earth, the total diameter of the universe is 414.2 million yojanas, not including the dimensions of the various heavenly bodies and lokas. The inclusion of these may be expected to bring this calculation in line with the figure of 500 million yojanas mentioned earlier.

Beyond the universe lies the limitless Pradhāna, which has within it countless other universes.

Purāṇic cosmology views the universe as going through cycles of creation and destruction of 8.64 billion years. The consideration of a universe of enormous size must have been inspired by a supposition of enormous age.

Reconciling Purāṇic and Standard Yojanas

It is clear that the Purāṇic yojana (y_p) are different from the Arthaśāstra yojana (y_s). To find the conversion factor, we equate the distances to the Sun.

$$0.4375 \times 10^6 \, y_s = 15.7 \times 10^6 \, y_p \quad (3)$$

In other words,

$$1 \, y_s \approx 36 \, y_p \quad (4)$$

The diameter of the Earth should now be about 875 x 36 ≈ 31,500 y_p. Perhaps, this was taken to be 32,000 y_p, twice the size of Meru. This understanding is confirmed by the statements in the Purāṇas. For example, MP 126 says that the size of Bhāratavarṣa (India) is 9,000 y_p, which is roughly correct.

We conclude that the kernel of the Purāṇic system is consistent with the Siddhāntas. The misunderstanding of it arose because attention was not paid to their different units of distance.

Speed of the Sun

Now that we have a Purāṇic context, Sāyaṇa's statement on the speed of 2,202 yojanas per half-nimeṣa can be examined.

We cannot be absolutely certain what yojanas did he have in mind: standard, or Purāṇic. But either way it is clear from the summary of Purāṇic cosmology that this speed could not be the speed of the Sun. At the distance of 15.7 million yojanas, Sun's speed is only 121.78 yojanas (y_p) per half-nimeṣa. Or if we use the the figure from VaP, it is 116.67. Converted into the standard yojanas, this number is only 3.24 y_s per half- nimeṣa.

Sāyaṇa's speed is about 18 times greater than the supposed speed of the Sun in y_p and 2×18^2 greater than the speed in y_s. So either way, a larger number with a definite relationship to the actual speed of the Sun was chosen for the speed of light.

The Purāṇic size of the universe is 13 to 16 times greater than the orbit of the Sun, not counting the actual sizes of the various heavenly bodies. Perhaps, the size was taken to be 18 times greater than the Sun's orbit. It seems reasonable to assume, then, that if the radius of the universe was taken to be about 282 million yojanas, a speed was postulated for light so that it could circle the farthest path in the universe within one day. This was the physical principle at the basis of the Purāṇic cosmology.

Concluding Remarks

We have seen that the astronomical numbers in the Purāṇas are much more consistent amongst themselves, and with the generally accepted sizes of the solar orbit, than has been hitherto assumed. The Purāṇic geography must not be taken literally.

We have also shown that the Sāyaṇa's figure of 2,202 yojanas per half- nimeṣa is consistent with Purāṇic cosmology where the size of "our universe" is a function of the speed of light. This size represents the space that can be spanned by light in one day.

It is quite certain that the figure for speed was obtained either by this argument or it was obtained by taking the postulated speed of the Sun in the Purāṇas and multiplying that by 18, or by multiplying the speed in standard yojanas by 2×18^2. We do know that 18 is a sacred number in the Purāṇas, and the fact that multiplication with this special number gave a figure that was in accord with the spanning of light in the universe in one day must have given it a special significance.

Is it possible that the number 2,202 arose because of a mistake of multiplication by 18 rather than a corresponding division (by 36) to reduce the Sun speed to standard yojanas? The answer to that must be "no" because such a mistake is too egregious. Furthermore, Sāyaṇa's own brother Mādhava was a distinguished astronomer and the incorrectness of this figure for the accepted speed of the Sun would have been obvious to him.

If Sāyaṇa's figure was derived from a postulated size of the universe, how was that huge size, so central to all Indian thought, arrived at? A possible explanation is that the physical size of the universe was taken to parallel the estimates of its age. These age-estimates were made larger and larger to postulate a time when the periods of all the heavenly bodies were synchronized [12].

The great numbers of the Purāṇas suggest that the concepts of *mahāyuga* and *kalpa*, sometimes credited to the astronomers of the Siddhāntic period, must have had an old pedigree. This is in consonance with the new understanding that considerable astronomy was in place in the second and the third millennia BC [13].

We have provided a context in which Sāyaṇa's speed can be understood. In this understanding, the speed of light was taken to be 2×18^2 greater than the speed of the Sun in standard yojanas so that light can travel the entire postulated size of the universe in one day. It is a lucky chance that the final number turned out to be exactly equal to the true speed. Sāyaṇa's value as speed of light must be considered the astonishing "blind hit" in the history of science!

Notes

1. Müller, Max (ed.), *Rig-Veda-Samhita together with the Commentary of Sāyaṇa*. Oxford University Press. London. 1890.
2. De, S.S., in *Issues in Vedic Astronomy and Astrology*. Pandya. H., Dikshit. S., Kansara. M.N. (eds.). Motilal Banarsidass. Delhi. 1992, pages 234-5;

   Vartak, P.V., *Scientific Knowledge in the Vedas*. Nag Publishers. Delhi, 1995.
3. Shrava, S., *History of Vedic Literature*. Pranava Prakashan, New Delhi. 1977, p. 185.
4. Larson, G.J. and Bhattacharya, R.S. (ed.). *Sāṃkhya: A Dualist Tradition in Indian Philosophy*. Princeton University Press. Princeton, 1987; Matilal, B.K., *Nyāya-Vaiśeṣika*, Otto Harrassowitz, Wiesbaden, 1977; Potter, K.H. (ed.). *Indian Metaphysics and Epistemology*, Princeton University Press, Princeton, 1977.

5. Seal, B., *The Positive Sciences of the Hindus*. Motilal Banarsidass, Delhi, 1985 (1915).
6. Kak, S.C., 1998, *Indian Journal of History of Science*, 33, in press.
7. Shukla, K.S. and Sarma, K.V., *Āryabhaṭiya of Āryabhaṭa*. Indian National Science Academy, New Delhi, 1976.
8. Shukla, K.S., *Āryabhaṭiya of Āryabhaṭa with the Commentary of Bhāskara I and Someśvara*, Indian National Science Academy, New Delhi, 1976, pp. 26-27.
9. Kak, S.C., *The Astronomical Code of the Ṛgveda*, Aditya, New Delhi, 1994.
10. Rocher, L., *The Purāṇas*, Otto Harrassowitz, Wiesbaden. 1986; Wilson, H.H. (tr.). *The Vishnu Purana*, Trubner & Co, London, 1865 (Garland Publishing, New York, 1981); *The Matsya Purāṇam*, The Pāṇini Office, Prayag, 1916 (AMS, New York. 1974); Tripathi, R.P. (tr.), *The Vāyu Purāṇa*, Hindi Sahitya Sammelan, Prayag, 1987.
11. de Santillana, G. and von Dechend, H., *Hamlet's Mill: An Essay on Myth and the Frame of Time*, Gambit, Boston. 1969.
12. Kak, S.C., *Vistas in Astronomy*, 36, 117-140, 1993.
13. Kak, S.C., *Quarterly Journal of the Royal Astronomical Society*, 36, 385-396, 1995; Kak, S.C., *Quarterly Journal of the Royal Astronomical Society*, 37, 709-715, 1996.

On the Science of Consciousness in Ancient India[††]

Subhash Kak

Introduction

Consciousness is described as the ultimate mystery in ancient Indian texts and its study is lauded as the highest science. But until recently, the question of consciousness was considered to lie outside of the scope of science [1] and, consequently, the references in the Indian texts to consciousness have not been examined for their significance to the history of science in India. But before a chronology of the ideas related to consciousness can be developed it is essential to understand their scientific significance and separate what can be correlated with the emerging insights of cognitive science from the more speculative philosophical and religious thought.

Scientific attitudes towards consciousness have changed due to the recent advances in neurophysiology and because modern physics and computer science are confronted with the question of the nature of the observer. In many ways, the study of consciousness is centre-stage in the discussions of modern science [2]. On the other hand, a considerable part of Indian thought is devoted to the question of consciousness. Although a part of this tradition deals with philosophical issues,

---

[††] Reprinted with permission from the author and the Indian National Science Academy

there are other aspects, as in yoga and tantra, that deal with structural aspects. Books such as *Yogavāsiṣṭha* and *Tripurarahasya* claim to describe the nature of consciousness. The same is generally true of various works on *yoga*, the *upaniṣads*, and even the earlier Vedic texts. The task for the historian of science is to sketch an evolution of the ideas related to consciousness and see how this sketch fits with the development of other scientific ideas. Since Indian works related to consciousness have not yet been systematically examined, it is perhaps premature to write such a history.

Note that there are intriguing parallels between the insights of the early Vedic theory of consciousness and those of quantum mechanics and neuroscience. In the Vedic theory, which dates back [3] to at least 2000 BC, one views awareness in terms of the reflection that the hardware of the brain provides to an underlying illuminating or awareness principle called the self. This approach allows one to separate questions of the tools of awareness, such as vision, hearing and the mind, from the person who obtains this awareness. The person is the conscious self, who is taken to be a reservoir of infinite potential. But the actual capabilities of the animal are determined by the neural hardware of its brain. This hardware may be compared to a mirror. The hardware of the human brain represents the clearest structure to focus the self, which is why humans are able to perform in ways that other animals cannot. Within the framework of this theory humans and other animals are persons and their apparent behavioral distinctions arise from the increased cloudedness of the neural hardware of the lower animals. Self-awareness is an emergent phenomenon which is grounded on the self and the associations stored in the brain.

From a modern scientific viewpoint, living systems are dynamic structures, that are defined in terms of their interaction with their environment. Their behavior is taken to reflect their past history in terms of instincts. Living systems can also be defined recursively in terms of living sub-systems. Thus, for ants, one may consider their society, an ant colony, as a living superorganism; in turn, the ant's sub-systems are also living. Such a recursive definition appears basic to all life. Machines, on the other hand, are based on networking of elements so as to instrument a well-defined computing procedure and they lack a recursive self definition.

The reality of consciousness is evident not only from the fact that responses are different in sleepwalking and awake states but from the considerable experimentation with split-brain patients [4]. The experiments of Kornhuber [5] indicate that it takes about eight-tenths of a second for the readiness potential to build up in the brain before voluntary action begins. According to Libet [6] the mind extrapolates back in time by about half a second or so the occurrence of certain events. So consciousness is not an epiphenomenon. As it possesses a unity, it should be described by a quantum mechanical wavefunction.

Eugene Wigner [7] argued that the laws of quantum mechanics may not apply to conscious agents. In a variant of the setting of the Schrödinger cat experiment, he visualized two conscious agents, one inside the box and another outside. If the inside agent makes an observation that leads to the collapse of the wavefunction, then how is the linear superposition of the states for the outside observer to be viewed? Wigner argued that in such a case, with a conscious observer as part of the system, linear superposition must not apply. This result, now called the Wigner's friend paradox, and others have led many quantum theorists to argue that basic advances in physics would eventually require one to include consciousness in the scientific framework.

The Vedic system, which was an earlier attempt to unify knowledge, was confronted by similar paradoxes. It is well known that Schrödinger's development of quantum mechanics was inspired, in part, by Vedānta [8], the full-blossomed Vedic system. His debt to the Vedic views is expressed in an essay he wrote in 1925 before he created his quantum theory:

> This life of yours which you are living is not merely a piece of this entire existence, but is in a certain sense the "whole"; only this whole is not so constituted that it can be surveyed in one single glance. This, as we know, is what the Brahmins express in that sacred, mystic formula which is yet really so simple and so clear: *tat tvam asi*, this is you. Or, again, in such words as "I am in the east and the west. I am above and below, I am this entire world." [9]

Schrödinger used Vedic ideas also in his immensely influential book "What is Life?" [10] that played a significant role in the development of modern biology. According to his biographer Walter Moore, there is a clear continuity between Schrödinger's understanding of Vedānta and his research:

> The unity and continuity of Vedanta are reflected in the unity and continuity of wave mechanics. In 1925, the world view of physics was a model of a great machine composed of separable interacting material particles. During the next few years, Schrödinger and Heisenberg and their followers created a universe based on superimposed inseparable waves of probability amplitudes. This new view would be entirely consistent with the Vedantic concept of All in One. [11]

In view of this connection between the Vedic system and quantum mechanics and the fact that quantum mechanical models of consciousness are being attempted, it is important to see how the Vedic philosophers developed their classification models of consciousness. A summary of one classification model is the main focus of the paper. The question of the history of ideas related to the notion of consciousness in ancient India will also be touched upon briefly in this paper.

Psychology, Complementarity

Self, Biology, Psychology

Neural network models have been used by cognitive scientists to model behaviour. The limitations of neural models have been highlighted by Sacks [12] and others who point out that these models do not take into account the notion of self.

The limitations of current theories of psychology were well summarized by the distinguished Canadian psychologist Melzack [13].

> The field of psychology is in a state of crisis. We are no closer now to understanding the most fundamental problems of psychology than we were

> when psychology became a science a hundred years ago. Each of us is aware of being a unique "self", different from other people and the world around us. But the nature of the "self", which is central to all psychology, has no physiological basis in any contemporary theory and continues to elude us. The concept of "mind" is as perplexing as ever....There is a profusion of little theories—theories of vision, pain, behaviour-modification, and so forth—but no broad unifying concepts... Cognitive psychology has recently been proclaimed as the revolutionary concept which will lead us away from the sterility of behaviourism. The freedom to talk about major psychological topics such as awareness and perceptual illusions does, indeed, represent a great advance over behaviourism. But on closer examination, cognitive psychology turns out to be little more than the psychology of William James published in 1890; some neuroscience and computer technology have been stirred in with the old psychological ingredients, but there have been no important conceptual advances.... We are adrift, without the anchor of neuropsychological theory, in a sea of facts—and practically drowning in them. We desperately need new concepts, new approaches.

Cognitive abilities arise from a continuing reflection on the perceived world and this question of reflection is central to the brain-mind problem, the measurement problem of physics, and the problem of determinism and free-will [14]. A dualist hypothesis [15] to explain brain-mind interaction or the process of reflection meets with the criticism that this violates the conservation laws of physics. On the other hand a brain-mind identity hypothesis, with a mechanistic or electronic representation of the brain processes, does not explain how self-awareness could arise. At the level of ordinary perception there exists a duality and complementarity between an autonomous (and reflexive) brain and a mind with intentionality.

Complementarity

The notion of self seems to hinge on an indivisibility akin to that found in quantum mechanics. The wave-particle duality encountered in quantum phenomena led Neils Bohr in 1927 to introduce the notion of complementarity. Complementarity is the principle that description of reality in any of the mutually contradictory pictures is incomplete; but between them such pictures form a complete, complementary description. This principle also presupposes that experiments can be unambiguously described only in classical terms. Considering the question of logical foundations of biology Bohr concluded that life (and also cognitive) processes are likewise subject to complementarity. The complementarity exhibited by life may be expressed most fundamentally between structure and behaviour.

> The recognition of the limitation of mechanical concepts in atomic physics would rather seem suited to conciliate the apparently contrasting viewpoints of physiology and psychology. Indeed, the necessity of considering the interaction between the measuring instruments and the object under investigation in atomic mechanics exhibits a close analogy to the peculiar difficulties in psychological analysis arising from the fact that the mental content is invariably altered when the attention is concentrated on any special feature of it. [16]

Bohr suggested an interesting analogy between neural (thought) and quantum processes. The instantaneous state of a thought may be compared with the position of a particle, whereas the direction of change of that thought may be compared with the particle's momentum. This is described by Bohm as follows [17]:

> Part of the significance of each element of a thought process appears to originate in its indivisible and incompletely controllable connections with other elements. Similarly, some of the characteristic properties of a quantum system (for instance, wave or particle nature) depend on indivisible and incompletely controllable quantum connections with surrounding objects. Thus, thought processes and quantum systems are analogous in that they can not be analyzed too much in terms of distinct elements, because the intrinsic nature of each element is not a property existing separately from and independently of other elements but is, instead, a property that arises partially from its relation with other elements.

There is also a similarity between the thought process and the classical limit of the quantum theory. The logical process corresponds to the most general type of thought process as the classical limit corresponds to the most general quantum process. In the logical process, we deal with classifications. These classifications are conceived as being completely separate but related by the rules of logic, which may be regarded as the analogue of the causal laws of classical physics. In any thought process, the component ideas are not separate but flow steadily and indivisibly. An attempt to analyze them into separate parts destroys or changes their meanings. Yet there are certain types of concepts, among which are those involving the classification of objects, in which we can, without producing any essential changes, neglect the indivisible and incompletely controllable connection with other ideas.

Complementarity is required at different levels of description. But just as one might use a probabilistic interpretation instead of complementarity for atomic descriptions, a probabilistic description may also be used for cognitive behaviour. However, such a probabilistic behaviour is inadequate to describe the behaviour of individual agents, just as notions of probability break down for individual objects.

As an epistemological principle complementarity has been criticized for not providing a unifying picture. But from an operational point of view complementarity, by considering all kinds of responses, becomes a very useful approach. When analyzed in terms of local interactions the framework of quantum mechanics suffers from other paradoxical characteristics. This shows up in non-local correlations that appear in the manner of action at a distance. [18]

The Vedic System of Knowledge

The Vedic system of knowledge appears already to be in place by the time of the Ṛgveda, conservatively dated to the late third or early second millennia BC [19]. The Ṛgveda and the other Vedic books do not present a logical resolution of the paradox of consciousness but assert that knowledge is of two types: it is superficially dual but at a deeper level it has a unity. The Vedic theory implies a complementarity by insisting that the material and the conscious are aspects of the same transcendent reality. The modern scientific tradition is like the Vedic tradition since it acknowledges contradictory or dual descriptions but seeks unifying explanations.

The Vedic approach to knowledge was based on the assumption that there exist equivalences of diverse kinds between the outer and the inner worlds. This prompted a deep examination of the human mind. In the description of physical reality the Vedic scholars noted several paradoxes [20]. If matter is divisible, each atom must be point-like because otherwise it would be further divisible. But how do point-like atoms lead to gross matter with size? Space is neither continuous nor discontinuous, for if it were continuous its points would be non-enumerable, but if it is discontinuous then how do objects move across the discontinuity? A popular way to express these difficulties was to talk about the riddle of being and becoming. The basic question here is how does an entity change its form and become another?

The philosophical systems that arose in India early on were meant to help one to find clues to the nature of consciousness. It was recognized that a complementarity existed between different approaches to reality, presenting contradictory perspectives. That is why philosophies of logic (*nyāya*) and physics (*vaiśeṣika*), cosmology and self (*Sāṅkhya*) and psychology (*yoga*), and language (*mimāṃsā*) and reality (*vedānta*) were grouped together in pairs. The system of *Sāṅkhya* considered a representation of matter and mind in different enumerative categories. The actual analysis of the physical world was continued outside of the cognitive tradition of *Sāṅkhya* in the sister system of *Vaiśeṣika*, that deals with further characteristics of the gross elements. The atomic doctrine of *Vaiśeṣika* can be seen to be an extension of the method of counting in terms of categories and relationships. The reality in itself was taken to be complex, continuous and beyond logical explanation. However, its representation in terms of the gross elements like space, mass (earth), energy (fire) and so on that are cognitively apprehendable, can be analyzed in discrete categories leading to atomicity. The cosmology of *Sāṅkhya* is really a reflection of the development of the mind, represented in cognitive categories.

The Greek philosophers also spoke of paradoxes inherent in descriptions. For example, we have Zeno's famed paradoxes on motion. But the Greek tradition does not appear to have dealt with the problem of consciousness.

The Vedic Model of the Mind

One Vedic model of the mind is expressed by the famous metaphor of the chariot in *Kaṭha Upaniṣad* and *Bhagavad Gītā*. A person is compared to a chariot that is pulled in different directions by the horses yoked to it; the horses represent the senses. The mind is the driver who holds the reins to these horses; but next to the mind sits the true observer, the self, who represents a universal unity. Without this self no coherent behaviour is possible.

The Five Levels

In the *Taittirīya Upaniṣad* an individual is represented in terms of five different sheaths or levels that enclose the individual's self. These levels, shown in an ascending order, are:

- The physical body (*annamaya koṣa*)
- Energy sheath (*prāṇamaya koṣa*)
- Mental sheath (*manomaya koṣa*)
- Intellect sheath (*vijñānamaya koṣa*)
- Emotion sheath (*ānandamaya koṣa*)

Here I have translated ānanda as emotion rather than the customary bliss, since emotion is the closest cognitive category to the Sanskrit term. These sheaths are defined at increasingly finer levels. At the highest level, above the emotion sheath, is the self. It is significant that emotion is placed higher than the intellect. This is a recognition of the fact that eventually meaning is communicated by associations which are influenced by the emotional state.

The energy that underlies physical and mental processes is called *prāṇa*. One may look at an individual in three different levels. At the lowest level is the physical body, at the next higher level is the energy systems at work, and at the next higher level are the thoughts. Since the three levels are interrelated, the energy situation may be changed by inputs either at the physical level or at the mental level. When the energy state is agitated and restless, it is characterized by *rajas*, when it is dull and lethargic, it is characterized by *tamas*. The state of equilibrium and balance is termed *sattva*.

Prāṇa, or energy, is described as the currency, or the medium of exchange, of the psychophysiological system. The levels 3, 4, and 5 are often lumped together and called the mind.

The key notion is that each higher level represents characteristics that are emergent on the ground of the previous level. In this theory mind is an emergent entity, but this emergence requires the presence of the self.

The Structure of the Mind

Now we consider the structural characteristics of the mind as given by the *Sāṅkhya* system. The mind is viewed as consisting of five components: *manas*, *ahaṃkāra*, *citta*, *buddhi* and *ātman*.

Manas is the lower mind which collects sense impressions. Its perceptions shift from moment to moment. This sensory-motor mind obtains its inputs from the senses of hearing, touch, sight, taste, and smell. Each of these senses may be taken to be governed by a separate agent.

Ahaṃkāra is the sense of I-ness that associates some perceptions to a subjective and personal experience.

Once sensory impressions have been related to I-ness by *ahaṃkāra*, their evaluation and resulting decisions are arrived at by *buddhi*, the intellect. *Manas*, *ahaṃkāra*, and *buddhi* are collectively called the internal instruments of the mind.

Next we come to *citta*, which is the memory bank of the mind. These memories constitute the foundation on which the rest of the mind operates. But *citta* is not merely a passive instrument. The organization of the new impressions throws up instinctual or primitive urges that creates different emotional states.

This mental complex surrounds the innermost aspect of consciousness which is called *ātman*. It is also called the self, *brahman*, or *jīva*. *Ātman* is considered to be beyond a finite enumeration of categories.

Hierarchical Levels within the Brain

Since the state of mind is mediated by the pranic energy, it becomes useful to determine how this is related to the focus on the various parts of the body. In the *tantras* seven, eight, or nine points of primary focus which are called *cakras* are described. It has been argued by some that the beginnings of this system go right back to the Vedic times as in *Atharvaveda* (10.2.31.-2) which describes the body as being eight-wheeled and nine-doored (*astacakrā navadvārā devānām pūryodhyā*). Their positions appear to be areas in the brain which map to different points on the spinal cord. The lowest one is located at the bottom of the vertebral column (*mūlādhāra cakra*). The next cakra is a few inches higher at the reproductive organs (*svādhisthāna cakra*). The third cakra (*maṇipura cakra*) is at the solar plexus. The heart region is the *anāhata cakra*. The throat has the fifth cakra called the *viśuddhi cakra*. Between the eyebrows is the *ājñā cakra*. At the top of the head is the *sahasrāra cakra* [21].

It may be assumed that the stimulation of these cakras in a proper way leads to the development of certain neural structures that allow the I-ness to experience the self. In other words, the *cakras* are points of basic focus inside the brain that lead to the explication of the cognitive process.

Further Universal Categories

If the categories of the mind are taken to arise from pattern recognition of shadow mental images, then how are these categories associated with a single "agent", and how does the mind bootstrap these shadow categories to find the nature of reality?

These questions were considered by later scholars who further developed the earlier Vedic ideas. This development occurred within the frameworks of *Vaiṣṇavism* as well as *Śaivism*. Here we speak of only one specific development that took place in Kashmir and has come to be known as Kashmir *Śaivism* [22]. The beginning of this specific tradition is seen in the *Śiva Sūtras* of Vasugupta (c. 800 AD). The *Śiva Sūtras* have aphorisms such as:

> *caitanyamātmā* (Consciousness is the self); *vidyāsamutthāne svābhāvike khecari śivāvasthā* (The knowledge of one's innate nature leads to Śiva's state: it is like wandering in the sky of consciousness).

Śiva is the name for the absolute or transcendental consciousness. Ordinary consciousness is bound by cognitive categories related to conditioned behaviour. By exploring the true springwells of ordinary consciousness one comes to recognise its universal (*Śiva*). This brings the further recognition that one is not a slave (*paśu*) of creation but its master (*pati*).

According to *Sāṅkhya*, reality may be represented in terms of twenty- five categories. These categories form the substratum of the classification in *Śaivism*. These categories are:

i. five elements of materiality, represented by earth, water, fire, air, ether;

ii. five subtle elements, represented by smell, taste, form, touch, sound;
iii. five organs of action, represented by reproduction, excretion, locomotion, grasping, speech;
iv. five organs of cognition, related to smell, taste, vision, touch, hearing;
v. three internal organs, being mind, ego, and intellect; and inherent nature (*prakṛti*), and consciousness (*puruṣa*).

These categories define the structure of the physical world and of agents and their minds. But this classification is not rich enough to describe the processes of consciousness as it is mentioned as a single category.

Śaivism enumerates further characteristics of consciousness:

i. sheaths or limitations of consciousness, being time (*kāla*), space (*niyati*), selectivity (*rāga*), awareness (*vidyā*), creativity (*kalā*), self forgetting (*māyā*), and
ii. five principles of the universal experience, which are correlation in the universal experience (*sadvidyā*; *śuddhavidyā*) identification of the universal (*īśvara*), the principle of being (*sādākhya*), the principle of negation and potentialization (*śakti*), and pure awareness by itself (*śiva*).

The first twenty-five categories relate to an everyday classification of reality where the initial five characteristics relate to the physical inanimate world, and the next eighteen define the characteristics of the conscious organism. The inherent nature of the individual is called prakrti while purusa represents self.

The next eleven categories characterize different aspects of consciousness which is to be understood in a sense different to that of mental capacities (categories 21, 22, 23). One of these mental capacities is akin to artificial intelligence of current computer science; which is geared to finding patterns and deciding between hypotheses. On the other hand categories 26 through 36 deal with interrelationships in space and time between these patterns and deeper levels of comprehension and awareness.

Any focus of consciousness must first be circumscribed by coordinates of time and space. Next, it is essential to select a process (out of the many defined) for attention (category 28). The aspect of consciousness that makes one have a feeling of inclusiveness with this process, followed later by a sense of alienation is called *māyā* (category 31). Thus *māyā* permits one, by a process of identification and detachment, to obtain limited knowledge (category 29) and to be creative (category 30).

Universal Experience

How does consciousness ebb and flow between an identity of self and an identity with the processes of the universe? According to *Śaivism*, a higher category (number 32) permits comprehension of oneness and separation with equal clarity. On the other hand category 33 allows a visualization of the ideal universe. Category 33 allows one to move beyond mere comprehension into a will to act. The final two categories deal with the potential energy that leads to continuing transformation (35) and pure consciousness by itself (36). Pure awareness is not to be understood as similar to everyday awareness of humans but rather as the underlying scheme that the laws of nature express. The laws themselves define the *śakti tattva*.

The cognitive categories of *Śaivism* are of relevance in computer science. At present only a subset of these categories can be dealt with by the most versatile computing machines. Current research is focused on the lower categories such as endowing machines with action capacities (as in robotics) and powers of sense perception (as in vision). At the higher levels, machines can be endowed with some capacity for judgement that typically involves computation of suitably framed cost functions, or finding patterns, of choosing between hypotheses, but the capacities of concretization and especially self-awareness seem to be completely, out of the realm of present day computing science.

A Theory of Speech and Cognition

The *Ṛgveda* (1.164.45) describes that speech and its concomitant cognition is of four kinds. The names of these kinds of speech are described by Bhartṛhari (c 450 AD) in his Vākyapādiya to be *vaikharī, madhyamā, paśyanti,* and *parā* [23]. *Vaikharī* represents gross sound; *madhyamā* is the level of mental images; *paśyanti* represents that gestalt or undifferentiated whole that sounds emerge from in the process of speaking and into which they merge in the process of hearing; *parā* is the unmanifest sound that resides in one's self or universal consciousness.

Bhartṛhari argues that reality (*sampratisattā*) when seen through the window of language reduces to a formal reality (*aupacārikī sattā*). Language can only deal upto the level of *paśyanti*, the gestalts underlying mental constructs, and it remains limited because *parā* speech lies beyond it.

Bhartṛhari calls the word or sentence considered an indivisible meaning unit as the *sphoṭa*. He bases this concept on the Vedic theory that speech (*vāk*) is a manifestation of the primordial reality. The word - *sphoṭa* is thus contrasted from word-sound. Meaning is obtained at a deep level based on the sequence of sounds.

The discovery of a very large number of phonetic symmetries in the first hymn of the *Ṛgveda* that cannot be conceived to have been deliberately introduced gives support to the thesis that language captures only some of the symmetries that nature's intelligence can express. Raster summarizes this discovery thus [24]:

> In our search for phonetic symmetries in the first sukta of the *Ṛgveda*, we examined the occurrence frequencies of more than 50 sound classes. Of these more than 40 sound classes were found with occurrence frequencies which are integral multiples of 8 and more than 20 sound classes with occurrence frequencies which are even integral multiples of 24... Moreover, in many cases, the occurrence frequencies of phonetically related sound classes form simple integral ratios, for example, the ratio of 2:1 between the frequencies of voiced and voiceless consonants and the ratio of 1:2 between the frequencies of long and short vowels. Thus, fundamental oppositions of the phonological system are reflected in the quantitative distribution of sounds in the text... The

> order which has been found underlying the phonological structure of the text is a hidden order. It cannot be perceived consciously while reading or listening to the text.... Although the order found in the distribution of the sounds in the text is unfolded sequentially in time, it is in itself not a linear, but a global phenomenon... (and) it is multidimensional.

Bhartṛhari's theory speaks of a reality richer than the expressive power of language. Like the observables of quantum theory, language picks only processes associated with its expressions.

The Vedic theory of consciousness speaks of a process of evolution. In this evolution the higher animals have a greater capacity to grasp the nature of the universe. The urge to evolve into higher forms is taken to be inherent in nature. A system of an evolution from inanimate to progressively higher life is clearly spelt out in the system of *Sāṅkhya*. At the mythological level this is represented by an ascent of *Viṣṇu* through the forms of fish, tortoise, boar, man-lion, the dwarf into man.

Concluding Remarks

The classificatory system developed in the Indian tradition does not address the paradoxes of consciousness. Rather, categories are defined, such as that of universal experience, that can be seen to explain the "complementary" nature of human experience. These categories clearly assign central role to selectivity, or context, and change. The Vedic system takes the mind to be emergent on the ground of the neural hardware of the brain, but this emergence is contingent on the principle of the self. In the earliest literature, the gods represent various cognitive centres. Tantric texts use esoteric diagrams or yantras for their representation [25]. There are other systems which are based on basic sounds of the alphabet related to fundamental aspects of the mind [26]. Such ideas have been, by tradition, consigned to philosophy or yoga and tantra. But it is possible, indeed likely, that there is much more than speculative thought in these models.

The tradition of consciousness study in India, long limited to philosophical studies, remains an unexplored frontier in the history of science. This paper is just an introduction to the problem. Further advances in a scientific understanding of consciousness will lead to a better appreciation of the Indian literature on the subject. One hopes that a comprehensive chronology of the various developments in the structural models of consciousness will be eventually produced.

Notes

1. Crick. F. and Koch, F., The problem of consciousness. *Scientific American*, 267(9), 153-159, 1992.

   Kak. S., Reflections in clouded mirrors: selfhood in animals and machines. *Symposium on Aliens, Apes, and Artificial Intelligence*. Southern Humanities Council Annual Conference. Huntsville. AL. February 1993.

   Goswami. A., *The Self Aware Universe*. New York: G. P. Putnam's Sons, 1993.

   Horgan. J., Can science explain consciousness? *Scientific American* 269(7), 88-94, 1994.

2. Edelman. G., *The Remembered Present: A Biological Theory of Consciousness*. New York: Basic Books. 1989.

Penrose. R., *Shadows of the Mind*. Oxford: Oxford University Press. 1994.

Scott. A. C., *Stairway to the Mind: The Controversial New Science of Consciousness*. New York: Springer-Verlag, 1995.

Kak, S., Quantum neural computing. *Advances in Imaging and Electron Physics*. 94. 250-313, 1995;

Kak, S., The three languages of the brain: quantum, reorganizational and associative. *4th Appalachian Conf. on Behavioral Neurodynamics*. Radford. VA, Sept. 1995.

Kak. S., Information physics, and computation. *Foundations of Physics*. 26. 127-137, 1996.

Kak, S., Why machines cannot be conscious. Presented at *Towards a Science of consciousness*. 1996. Tucson, April 1996.

Hameroff, S. and Penrose. R., Conscious events as orchestrated spacetime selections. *Journal of Consciousness Studies*. 3, 36-53. 1996.

3. Kak. S.C., *The Astronomical Code of the Ṛgveda*. New Delhi: Aditya, 1994.

   Feuerstein. G., Kak. S., Frawiey. D., *In Search of the Cradle of Civilization*. Wheaton: Quest Books. 1995.

4. Trevarthen. C. (Ed.), *Brain Circuits and Functions of the Mind: Essays in Honor of Roger W. Sperry*. Cambridge: Cambridge University Press. 1990.

5. Kornhuber. H.H., Cerebral cortex, cerebellum, and basal ganglia: An introduction to their motor function. In W. Schmitt (ed.), *The Neurosciences: Third Study Program*. Cambridge: MIT Press. 1974.

6. Libet. B., Electrical stimulation of cortex in human subjects, and conscious sensory aspects. In A. lggo (ed.), *Handbook of sensory physiology: Vol. II.*

Somatosensory System. New York: Springer-Verlag. 1973.

7. Wigner, E., *Symmetries and Reflections*. Bloomington: Indiana University Press, 1967.
8. Schrödinger, E., *Meine Weltansicht.* Wien: Paul Zsolnay, 1961.
9. Moore, W., Schrödinger, *Life and Thought.* Cambridge University Press. 1989, pp. 170-3.
10. Schrödinger, E., *What is Life?* New York: Macmillan, 1965.
11. Moore op. cit. pp. 173.
12. Sacks, O., *Awakenings, A Leg to Stand On, The Man Who Mistook His Wife for a Hat.* New York: Book of the Month Club, 1990.
13. Melzack. R., Phantom limbs, the self and the brain. *Canadian Psychology*, 30, 1-16, 1989, pp 1-2.
14. Kak, S.C., *The Nature of Physical Reality*. New York: Peter Lang. 1986.

    Penrose, R., *The Emperor's New Mind: Concerning Computers, Minds, and the Laws of Physics*. Oxford University Press, 1989.
15. Eccles, J.C., Do mental events cause neural events analogously to the probability fields of quantum mechanics? *Proc. Society London*, B 227,411-428, 1986.
16. Bohr, N., *Atomic Physics and Human Knowledge*. New York: Science Editions, 1961.
17. Bohm, D., *Quantum Theory*. New York: Prentice-Hall, 1951.
18. Bell. J.S., *Speakable and Unspeakable in Quantum Mechanics.* Cambridge: Cambridge University Press. 1987.
19. Feuerstein et al, op cit.
20. Kak. S.C., *The Nature of Physical Reality*, op. cit.

21. Feuersiein, G., *Yoga*. Los Angeles: Jeremy P. Tarcher, 1989.

22. Abhinavagupla, R., *A Trident of Wisdom*. Albany: State University of New York Press, 1989.

    Singh, Jaideva. *Śiva Sūtras*. Delhi; Motilal Banarsidass. 1979.

    Dyczkowski, M.S.G., *The Doctrine of Vibration*. Albany: SUNY Press, 1987.

23. Abhyankar, K.V. and Limaye, V.P., *Vākyapadīya of Bhartṛhari*. Poona: University of Poona. 1965.

    Coward. H.G., *Bhartṛhari*. Boston: Twayne Publishers. 1976.

24. Raster, P., *Phonetic Symmetries in the First Hymn of the Rigveda*. Innsbruck. 1992. p. 38.

25. Woodroffe, J., *The Serpent Power*. Madras: Ganesh and Co., 1981.

    Feuerstein, op cit.

26. Abhinavagupta. *Parātriśikā-Vivaraṇa*. Delhi: Motilal Banarsidass, 1988.

General Notes

The citation information about the previously published papers in this volume is as follows:

Chap. 3 "Binary Numbers in Indian Antiquity"
Journal of Indian Philosophy, Vol. 21, pp. 31-50, 1993.

Chap. 4 "The Katapayadi Formula and the Modern Hashing Technique"
IEEE Annals of the History of Computing, Vol. 19, pp. 49-52, 1997.

Chap. 6 "Pāṇini Tested by Fowler's Automaton"
JAOS, Vol. 85, pp. 44-47, 1965. It has also been reprinted in *Universals*, Studies in Indian Logic and Linguistics, University of Chicago Press, Chicago, 1988.

Chap. 7 "Formal Structures in Indian Logic"
Synthese, Vol. 12, pp. 279-286, 1960. It was reprinted in *Universals*: Studies in Indian Logic and Linguistics, University of Chicago Press, Chicago, 1988. The note is from a recent work that will appear in a forthcoming book entitled *Giant Leaps into the Realm of Knowing*.

Chap. 8 "Planets in The Vedic Literature"
Indian Journal of History of Science, Vol. 29, pp. 495-506, 1997.

Chap. 10 "On The Science of Consciousness in Ancient India"
Indian Journal of History of Science, Vol. 32, pp. 105-120, 1997.

Bibliography

Abhinavagupta. 1988. *Parātriśikā-Vivaraṇa*. Delhi: Motilal Banarsidass.

Abhinavagupla, R. 1989. *A Trident of Wisdom*. Albany: State University of New York Press.

Abhyankar, K.V. and Limaye. 1965. V.P., *Vākyapadīya of Bhartṛhari*. Poona: University of Poona.

Apte, V. S. 1959. *The Practical Sanskrit-English Dictionary*. 3 vols. Poona: Prasad Prakashan.

Backus, John. 1959. The syntax and semantics of the proposed international algebraic language of the Zurich ACM-GAMM conference. *Proc. Internat. Conf. Inf. Proc.*, UNESCO, Paris.

Bag, A. K. 1979. *Mathematics in Ancient and Medieval India*. Varanasi: Chaukhambha Orientalia.

Ballantyne, J. R. (ed.). 1891. *Laghukaumudī*. Benares, ii.

Bell. J.S. 1987. *Speakable and Unspeakable in Quantum Mechanics*. Cambridge: Cambridge University Press.

Bharati, Sri Ramacandra, ed. 1908. *Vṛttaratnākara by Pandit Kedārabhaṭṭa, with its Commentary Vṛttaratnākarapañcikā*. Bombay: Nirnaya-Sagar Press.

Billard, R. 1971. *L 'astronomie Indienne*. Paris.

Bochenski, I.M. 1956. *Formale Logik*, Freiburg/München.

Bodas, Rajaram Shastri, ed. 1917. *The Yogasūtras of Patañjali with the Scholium of Vyāsa*. Bombay Sanskrit and Prakrit Series No. XLVI. Bombay: Government Central Press: 131-132.

Bohm, D. 1951. *Quantum Theory*. New York: Prentice-Hall.

Bohr, N. 1961. *Atomic Physics and Human Knowledge*. New York: Science Editions.

Boudon, P. 1938. *"Une application du raisonnement par l'absurde dans l'interpretation de Pāṇini"* J A 230, 65-121: 72-8.

Brown, J.W. 1994. Morphogenesis and mental process. *Development and Psychopathology*. vol. 6, 551-563.

Bühler, J. Georg. 1904. "Indian Paleography", (trl. from the German by J. F. Fleet). *Indian Antiquary* 33. Appendix.: 1-102.

Buiskool, H. E. 1939. *pūrvatrāsiddham: Analytisch onderzoek aangaande het systeem der Tripādi van Pāṇini's Aṣṭādhyayī, Amsterdam 1934; the same, The Tripādi, being an abridged English recast of Pūrvatrāsiddham (An analytical-synthetical inquiry into the system of the last three chapters of Pāṇini's Aṣṭādhyayī*), Leiden.

Burrow, T. 1955. *The Sanskrit language*. London.

Chomsky, N. 1965. "Three models for the description of language," reprinted in: *Readings in mathematical psychology*. II. ed. Luce, Bush & Galanter, New York & London. 105- 124.

Chomsky, N. and G. A. Miller. 1963. "Introduction to the formal analysis of natural languages", *Handbook of mathematical psychology*, II, ed. Luce, Bush & Galanter. New York & London.

Closs. Michael P. 1986. *Native American Mathematics*. Austin: University of Texas Press.

Couturat, Louis. ed. 1903. Opuscules et fragments inédits de Leibniz, extraits des manuscrits de la Bibliotheque royale de Hanovre par Louis Couturat ... Paris: Alcan.

Coward. H.G. 1976. *Bhartṛhari*. Boston: Twayne Publishers.

Crick. F. and Koch, F. 1992. The problem of consciousness. *Scientific American*, 267(9), 153-159.

Datta, Bibhutibhusan and Avadesh N. Singh. 1935. *History of Indian Mathematics*. 2 vols; repr. 1 vol. 1962. Bombay: Asian Publishing House.

de S.G. and von Dechend, H. 1969. *Hamlet's Mill: An Essay on Myth and the Frame of Time*, Gambit, Boston.

De, S.S. 1992. *Issues in Vedic Astronomy and Astrology*. Pandya. H., Dikshit. S., Kansara. M.N. (eds.). Motilal Banarsidass. Delhi, 234-5.

Dyczkowski, M.S.G. 1987. *The Doctrine of Vibration*. Albany: SUNY Press.

Eccles, J.C. 1986. Do mental events cause neural events analogously to the probability fields of quantum mechanics? *Proc. Society London*, B 227,411-428.

Edelman. G. 1989. *The Remembered Present: A Biological Theory of Consciousness*. New York: Basic Books.

Feuerstein, G. 1989. *Yoga*. Los Angeles: Jeremy P. Tarcher.

Feuerstein, G., S. Kak and D. Frawley, 1995. *In Search of the Cradle of Civilization*. Wheaten: Quest Books.

Filliozat, J. 1970. The expansion of Indian medicine abroad. In Lokesh Chandra (ed.) *India's Contributions to World Thought and Culture.* Madras: Vivekananda Memorial Committee. 67-70.

Francfort, H.-P. 1992. Evidence for Harappan irrigation system in Haryana and Rajasthan. *Eastern Anthropologist.* vol. 45, 87-103.

Frawley, D. 1993. *Gods. Sages and Kings: Vedic Secrets of Ancient Civilization.* Delhi, India: Motilal Banarsidass.

Frawley, D. 1994. Planets in the Vedic literature. *Indian Journal of History of Science.* vol. 29, 495-506.

Gokhale, Sh. L. 1966. *Indian Numerals.* Poona: Deccan College Silver Jubilee Series No. 43. Chart nos. 4, 6, 14, 20.

Goswami. A. 1993. *The Self Aware Universe.* New York: G. P. Putnam's Sons.

Hameroff, S. and Penrose. R. 1996. Conscious events as orchestrated spacetime selections. *Journal of Consciousness Studies.* 3, 36-53.

Horgan. J. 1994. Can science explain consciousness? *Scientific American* 269(7), 88-94.

Houston, Vyaas (1991). Foreword to "*Gods, Sages and Kings*" by David Frawley, Passage Press, Salt Lake City, Utah.

Ifrah, Georges. 1985. *From One to Zero.* New York: Viking Penguin Inc.

Indraji, Bhagavanlal. 1876. "On Ancient Nagari Numeration; from an Inscription at Naneghat". *Journal of the Bombay Branch of the Royal Asiatic Society* 12: 404-406.

Ingalls, D. H. H. 1951. *Materials for the study of Navya-nyāya logic*, Cambridge, Mass., USA.

Ingerman, P.Z. (1966). *A Syntax-Oriented Translator*, Academic Press, New York.

Ingerman, P.Z. 1967 "Pāṇini-Backus Form Suggested," *Comm. ACM* 10, 3, p. 137.

Jacobi, Hermann. 1933. "Uber die ältesten indischen Metriker und ihr Werk." *Indian Linguistics: Grierson Comm. Volume*. Lahore: 131- 141.

Kak, S. 1986. *The Nature of Physical Reality*. New York: Peter Lang.

Kak, S. 1987. The Pāṇinian approach to natural language processing. *Intl. Journal of Approximate Reasoning*, vol. 1, 117-130.

Kak, S. 1993. Reflections in clouded mirrors: selfhood in animals and machines. *Symposium on Aliens, Apes, and Artificial Intelligence*. Southern Humanities Council Annual Conference. Huntsville, AL, USA.

Kak, S. 1993. "Astronomy in the Śatapatha Brāhmaṇa. *Indian J. of History of Science*, 28, 15-34.

Kak, S. 1993. "The structure of the Ṛgveda", *Indian J. of History of Science*, 28. 71-79.

Kak, S. 1994a. *The Astronomical Code of the Ṛgveda*. New Delhi: Aditya.

Kak, S. 1994b. The evolution of writing in India. *Indian Journal of History of Science*. vol. 28, 375-388.

Kak, S. 1994c. *India at Century's End*. New Delhi: VOI.

Kak, S. 1995. Quantum neural computing. *Advances in Imaging and Electron Physics*. 94. 250-313.

Kak, S. 1995. The three-languages of the brain: quantum, reorganizational and associative. *4th Appalachian Conf. on Behavioral Neurodynamics*. Radford. VA.

Kak, S. 1995a. The astronomy of the age of geometric altars. *Quarterly Journal of the Royal Astronomical Society*. vol. 36, 385-396.

Kak, S. 1995b. From Vedic science to Vedanta. *The Adyar Library Bulletin*. vol. 59, 1-36.

Kak, S. 1996. Information physics, and computation. *Foundations of Physics*. 26. 127-137.

Kak, S. 1996. Why machines cannot be conscious. Presented at *Towards a Science of consciousness. Tucson, Arizona, USA.*

Kak, S. 1996a. Knowledge of planets in the third millennium B.C. *Quarterly Journal of the Royal Astronomical Society*. vol. 37, 709-715.

Kak, S. 1996b. The three languages of the brain. In Pribram, K.H. and J. King (eds.) *Learning as Self-Organization*. Mahwah, NJ: Lawrence Erlbaum.

Kak, S. 1997a. *The rhythms of consciousness*. Quest. vol. 10, 52-56.

Kak, S. I997b. Aspects of science in ancient India. In Sridhar, S. and N. Mattoo (eds.) *Ananya: A Portrait of India*. New York: AIA, 399-420.

Kak, S. 1997c. Archaeoastronomy and literature. Current Science. vol. 73, 624-627.

Kak, S. 1997d. On the science of consciousness in ancient India. *Indian Journal of History of Science*. vol. 32, 105-120.

Kavyatirtha, N.R.A. (Ed.). (1954). Pāṇinimunipranitah astadhyayisutrapathah vartikapathasamalankrtah (Pāṇini—Reading of Rules in Eight Chapters, Embellished by His Pupils). Bombay, India.

Keith, Arthur Berriedale. 1914. *The Veda of the Black Yajus School*. Cambridge: Harvard Oriental Series 19 Part II: 350-351.

Kennedy, K.A.R. 1995. Have Aryans been identified in the prehistoric skeletal record from South Asia? In Erdosy. G. (ed.). *The Indo-Aryans of South Asia*. Berlin: Walter de Gruyter, 32-66.

Kornhuber. H.H. 1974. Cerebral cortex, cerebellum, and basal ganglia: An introduction to their motor function. In W. Schmitt (ed.), *The Neurosciences: Third Study Program*. Cambridge: MIT Press.

Knuth, D. 1964. Backus normal form vs. Backus Naur form. *Comm. ACM* 7, 12, 735-736.

Lal, B.B. 1997. *The Earliest Civilization of South Asia*. New Delhi: Aryan International.

Larson, G.J. and Bhattacharya, R.S. (ed.). 1987. *Sāṃkhya: A Dualist Tradition in Indian Philosophy*. Princeton University Press, Princeton, New Jersey, USA.

Libet. B. 1973. Electrical stimulation of cortex in human subjects, and conscious sensory aspects. In A. Iggo (ed.), *Handbook of sensory physiology: Vol. II. Somatosensory System*. New York: Springer-Verlag.

Loosen, Renate and Franz Vonessen, ed. 1968. *Gottfried Wilhelm Leibniz. Zwei Briefe über das Binäre Zahlensystem und die Chinesische Philosophie*. Stuttgart: Belser-Presse.

Marcotty, M. & Ledgard, H. (1986). *The World of Programming Languages*, Springer-Verlag, Berlin, p. 41.

Matilal, B.K. 1968. *The Navva-Nyaya Doctrine of Negation*. Cambridge: Harvard University Press.

Matilal, B.K. 1977. *Nyāya-Vaiśeṣika*, Otto Harrassowitz, Wiesbaden.

McClain. E.G. 1978. *The Myth of Invariance*. Boulder: Shambhala.

Melzack. R. 1989. Phantom limbs, the self and the brain. *Canadian Psychology*, 30, 1-16, pp 1-2.

Moore, W. 1989. *Schrödinger, Life and Thought*. Cambridge University Press.

Müller, Max (ed.). 1890. *Rig-Veda-Samhita together with the Commentary of Sāyaṇa*. Oxford University Press. London.

Nāgojībhatta. 1874. *Paribhāsenduśekhara*. ed. F. Kielhorn. II, Translation and Notes. Bombay.

Naur, Peter (Ed.) (1963). Revised report on the algorithmic language ALGOL 60, *Comm. ACM* 6, 1, 1-17.

Penrose, R. 1989. *The Emperor's New Mind: Concerning Computers, Minds, and the Laws of Physics*. Oxford University Press.

Penrose. R. 1994. *Shadows of the Mind*. Oxford: Oxford University Press.

Potter, K.H. (ed.). 1977. *Indian Metaphysics and Epistemology*, Princeton University Press, Princeton, New Jersey, USA.

Rajaram, N. and D. Frawley. 1994. *Vedic Aryans and the Origins of Civilization.* St Hyacinthe, Canada: World Hentage Press.

Raster, P. 1992. *Phonetic Symmetries in the First Hymn of the Rigveda.* Innsbruck.

Renou, L. 1955. *Études védiques et Pāninéennes.* I, Paris.

Renou, L. 1956. *Études védiques et Pāninéennes.* II, Paris.

Resnikoff, H.L. and R.O. Wall. 1984. Mathematics in Civilization (2nd Ed.), Dover Publ.

Rocher, L. 1986. *The Purāṇas,* Otto Harrassowitz, Wiesbaden.

Sacks, O. 1990. *Awakenings, A Leg to Stand On, The Man Who Mistook His Wife for a Hat.* New York: Book of the Month Club.

Sarma, K.V. 1985. A survey of source materials. *Indian Journal of History of Science.* vol. 20, 1-20.

Schayer, S. 1933. *Über die Methode der Nyāya-Forchung,* Festschrift M. Winternitz. Leipzig.

Schrödinger, E. 1961. *Meine Weltansicht.* Wien: Paul Zsolnay.

Schrödinger, E. 1965. *What is Life?* New York: Macmillan.

Scott. A. C. 1995. *Stairway to the Mind: The Controversial New Science of Consciousness.* New York: Springer-Verlag.

Seal, B. 1985 (1915). *The Positive Sciences of the Hindus.* Motilal Banarsidass, Delhi.

Seidenberg, A. 1962. The ritual origin of geometry. *Archive for History of Exact Sciences.* vol. 1, 488-527.

Seidenberg, A. 1978. The origin of mathematics. *Archive for History of Exact Sciences*. 18, 301-342.

Seidenberg, A. 1986. "The Zero in the Mayan Numerical Notation," in *Michael Closs* 1986 pp. 371-386.

Selenius, C-O. 1975. Rationale of the chakravala process of Jayadeva and Bhaskara II. *Historia Mathematica*. vol. 2, 167-184.

Sen, S. 1924. A study on Mathurānātha's *Tattva-cintāmaṇi-rahasya*. Wageningen.

Sengupta, P.C. 1947. *Ancient Indian Chronology*. Calcutta: University of Calcutta Press.

Shaffer, J. and D.L. Lichtenstein. 1995. The concept of "cultural tradition" and "paleoethnicity" in South Asian archaeology. In Erdosy, G. (ed.), *The Indo-Aryans of South Asia*. Berlin: Waiter de Gruyter, 126-154.

Shankar, Kripa, ed., trans. 1976. *Aryabhatiya of Aryabhata*. New Delhi: the Indian National Science Academy.

Sharma, Aryendra, K. Deshpande and D. G. Padhye, ed. 1969. *Vṛttaratnākara of Śrī Kedāra Bhaṭṭa*. Hyderabad: Osmania University.

Shefts, B. 1963. *Grammatical method in Pāṇini: His treatment of Sanskrit present stems*. New Haven 1961: cf. Lg 39, 483-8.

Sircar, D. C. 1965. *Indian Epigraphy*. Delhi: Motilal Banarsidass.

Shrava, S. 1977. *History of Vedic Literature*. Pranava Prakashan, New Delhi.

Shukla, K.S. and Sarma, K.V. 1976. *Āryabhaṭiya of Āryabhaṭa*. Indian National Science Academy, New Delhi.

Singh, J. 1979. *Śiva Sūtras*. Delhi; Motilal Banarsidass.

Staal, J.F. 1958. "Means of formalisation in Indian and Western logic", Proceedings of the XIIth International Congress of Philosophy, Venice.

Staal, J.F. 1960. *Indo-lranian Journal* 4, 68-73

Staal, J.F. 1962. "Negation and the law of contradiction: a comparative study", *BSOAS* 25, 53-6.

Staal, J.F. 1965. "Context-sensitive rules in Pāṇini", *Foundations of Language* 1, 63-72.

Staal, J.F. 1988. *Universals*. Chicago: University of Chicago Press.

Trevarthen. C. (Ed.). 1990. *Brain Circuits and Functions of the Mind: Essays in Honor of Roger W. Sperry*. Cambridge: Cambridge University Press.

Tripathi, R.P. (tr.). 1987. *The Vāyu Purāṇa*, Hindi Sahitya Sammelan, Prayag, India.

Tyagi, G.S. 1992. "Decorative intricate patterns in Indian rock art." in *Rock Art in the Old World*. ed. M. Lorblanchet, 303-317. New Delhi.

van Nooten, B. 1993. Binary numbers in Indian antiquity. *Journal of Indian Philosophy*, vol. 21, 31-50.

Vartak, P.V. 1995. *Scientific Knowledge in the Vedas*. Delhi: Nag Publishers.

Vasu, S.C. (1962). The Aṣṭādhyayī, Motilal Banarsidass, Delhi, India.

Velankar, H.D. (1949). *Kedāraviracito Vṛttaratnākaraḥ in Jayadaman*. Bombay: Haritosha Samiti.

Wakankar, V.S. 1992. "Rock painting in India." in *Rock Art in the Old World*, ed. M. Lorblanchet. 319-336. New Delhi.

Weber, Albrecht. 1863. Über die Metrik der Inder. *Indische Studien* No. 8. Berlin.

Wigner, E. 1967. *Symmetries and Reflections*. Bloomington: Indiana University Press.

Wilson, H.H. (tr.). 1865. *The Vishnu Purana*, Trubner & Co, London, UK. (Garland Publishing, New York, 1981).

Wilson, H.H. (tr.). 1916. *The Matsya Purāṇam*, The Pāṇini Office, Prayag, India. (AMS, New York. 1974).

Woodroffe, J. 1981. *The Serpent Power*. Madras: Ganesh and Co.

Woods, James H., trans. 1914. The Yoga-system of Patañjali, Cambridge: *Harvard Oriental Series* 17.

Index

Notes on Contributors‡‡

David Frawley is the Director of the American Institute of Vedic Studies. He is the author of numerous books including *Gods, Sages and Kings* and *co-author of In Search of the Cradle of Civilization.*

Subhash Kak is Regents Professor at Oklahoma State University in Stillwater. His books include *The Nature of Physical Reality* and *the Astronomical Code of the Ṛgveda.*

Anand Raman is Professor at the Department of Computer Science at Massey University in New Zealand.

T.R.N. Rao is the Z.L. Loflin Chair Emeritus Professor of Computer Science at the University of Louisiana in Lafayette. He has authored books such as *Error-Codes for Arithmetic Processors* and *Error-Control Coding for Computer Systems.*

J. Frits Staal is Professor of Philosophy at the University of California at Berkeley. He is the author of several books that include *Agni: The Vedic Ritual of the Fire Altar, Universals,* and *Rules without Meaning.*

Barend A. van Nooten is Professor of Sanskrit at the University of California at Berkeley. He is the co-author of *Rigveda: A Metrically Restored Text.*

---

‡‡ Affiliations of the non-editor contributors are those at the time of the original publication of the book